Teacher's Resource Masters

ACCELERATED GRADE 7
VOLUME 1

Topics 1-6
Home-School Connection Letters
Pick a Project
enVision® STEM Project
Reteach to Build Understanding
Additional Vocabulary Support
Build Mathematical Literacy
Enrichment

enVision® Mathematics

SAVVAS
LEARNING COMPANY

ISBN-13: 978-0-7685-6566-9
ISBN-10: 0-7685-6566-9

4 20

Grade 7 Accelerated
Volume 1: Topics 1–6

Topic 5 **Generate Equivalent Expressions**

Topic 6 **Solve Problems Using Equations and Inequalities**

Name _____

Rational Number Operations

Dear Family,

   Your child is learning to add, subtract, multiply, and divide integers and rational numbers. The focus is on understanding positive and negative numbers and how the signs of the numbers affect their sums, differences, products, and quotients. He or she will use a variety of methods and tools, including number lines, absolute value, and inverse operations, to develop an understanding of these operations.

   Here is an activity you can do with your child to help him or her develop fluency with integers.

What's the Sum?

Materials: 21 index cards or small pieces of paper numbered with the integers from −10 to 10 (one integer per card)

Step 1 Player 1 shuffles the cards and gives two cards to Player 2.

Step 2 Player 2 adds the numbers on his or her cards and explains how the signs of the numbers affect the sum. For example, $3 + (-7) = -4$.

Step 3 Player 2 returns the cards to the stack. Trade roles and play again.

Alternate Gameplay: Subtract, multiply, or divide the integers.

Observe Your Child

Focus on Mathematical Practices
Reason abstractly and quantitatively.

Help your child become proficient with this Mathematical Practice. Ask your child to suggest a real-world context for each sum in the game. If he or she has difficulty coming up with a context, you might discuss saving and spending money or changes in temperature or elevation.

Nombre _____

Operaciones con número racionales

De la escuela al hogar
(en español)

Tema **1**

Estimada familia:

Su hijo o hija está aprendiendo a sumar, restar, multiplicar y dividir enteros y números racionales. Este tema se enfoca en la comprensión de los números positivos y negativos, y el modo en que los signos de los números afectan sus sumas, diferencias, productos y cocientes. Su hijo o hija aplicará diversos métodos y herramientas, como rectas numéricas, valor absoluto y operaciones inversas, para desarrollar su comprensión de esas operaciones.

Esta es una actividad que puede realizar con su hijo o hija para ayudarlo(a) a adquirir fluidez con los enteros.

¿Cuál es la suma?

Materiales: 21 tarjetas de fichero o pedazos de papel numerados con los enteros del –10 al 10 (un entero por tarjeta)

Paso 1 El Jugador 1 mezcla las tarjetas y le da dos al Jugador 2.

Paso 2 El Jugador 2 suma los números de sus tarjetas y explica cómo influyen en la suma los signos de los números. Por ejemplo: $3 + (-7) = -4$.

Paso 3 El Jugador 2 devuelve las tarjetas a la pila. Los jugadores intercambian los roles y juegan otra vez.

Modo de juego alternativo: Los jugadores restan, multiplican o dividen los enteros.

Observe a su hijo o hija

Enfoque en las Prácticas matemáticas
Razonar de manera abstracta y cuantitativa.

Ayude a su hijo o hija a adquirir competencia en esta Práctica matemática. Pídale que sugiera un contexto de la vida diaria para cada suma del juego. Si tiene dificultades para imaginar un contexto, pueden conversar sobre ahorrar y gastar dinero, o cambios de temperatura o de altitud.

Handmade to Sell

Before the Industrial Revolution of the 18th century, goods that were bought, sold, and used were all made by hand. Today, although most goods are made in factories, many craftspeople still make and sell handcrafted goods. Craftspeople today sell their goods in local shops, at craft fairs, and in online shops.

Being a successful craftsperson involves more than being skilled at a craft and having an artistic eye. Craftspeople have to understand budgets to ensure that they can make a worthwhile profit from their work. They must keep track of expenses (negative values) and income (positive values). By paying close attention to their budget and the quality of their product, craftspeople can maximize their profits.

Your Project **Design a Handmade Item to Sell**

What can you make that someone might want to buy? Can you make beaded jewelry? A painting? Build something? What materials will you need? What do you think the right sales price for your item would be?

Design a handmade item to sell. Make a sample item. Calculate how much the item costs to make, and set a selling price. Develop a budget for your craft business. Your budget should use both positive and negative rational numbers to show how much money you can make if you sell 1, 5, 25, and 100 items. Determine how many items you have to sell to make a profit. Explain why you chose your selling price. Use this information to write up a business proposal.

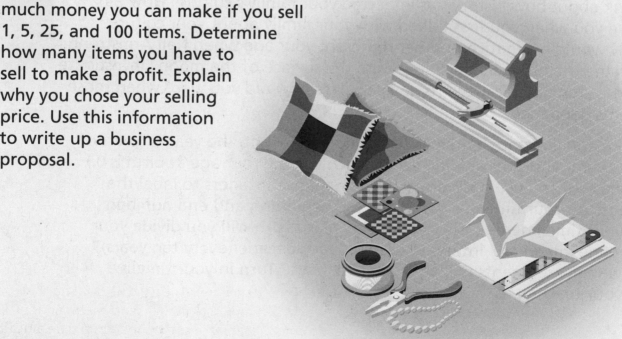

Name _____

A Sign of the Times

What does time mean to you? Do you think of your life in terms of minutes or in terms of events? How would a picture of how you spend your time during one day differ from a picture of how you spend your time during one year?

A timeline is one way to tell a story and give a quick summary of events in chronological order. Some timelines are lists, while others are diagrams. People use timelines to summarize events in their lives, historical events, or projects they want to do. Timelines can show how events do or do not overlap, how much time there is between events, and the amount of time each event takes.

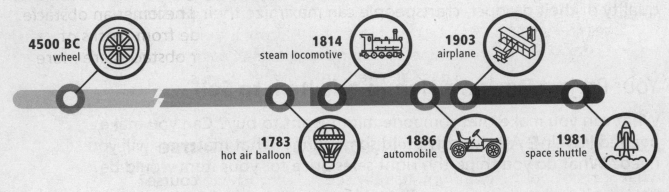

4500 BC wheel
1783 hot air balloon
1814 steam locomotive
1886 automobile
1903 airplane
1981 space shuttle

Your Project **Make a Timeline**

Think about how history has impacted your family's culture. How old were you when you first talked with your family about your culture? How would a negative number represent your age when Neil Armstrong became the first person to step onto the surface of the moon? Investigate at least ten historical events and calculate how old you were when those events happened.

Make and illustrate a timeline showing each event, the year or years of the event, and your age in years at each event. (Your age at birth is 0.) Make sure you use both positive and negative integers to label the events on your timeline. What will the beginning and end numbers of your time line be (using your birth year as 0)? Will you divide your timeline into yearly intervals, or mark each decade (every ten years)? How many segments will your timeline have? Turn in your timeline to your teacher.

Name _____

Warrior Zone

An obstacle course is a series of challenges a person must complete in a certain order or within a given amount of time. Most obstacle courses include tasks that require diverse skills, agility, and strength. Some obstacle courses are designed to be run independently, and some are set up to be completed by teams.

Sometimes an obstacle course must be completed without falling or touching the ground, while other courses are flooded so that mud becomes an obstacle. Some obstacles are simple, made from blocks of wood or lengths of rope. Other obstacles are more complicated, made with frames.

Your Project **Build a Model of an Obstacle Course**

What sorts of obstacles do you usually see on an obstacle course? What makes an obstacle course interesting? What makes it challenging? What makes it fun?

Decide what challenges to include in your obstacle course. The starting point of your obstacle course must be above the ground. Research possible building materials for your obstacle course and how much those materials cost. Produce a model of your obstacle course and designs of at least two challenges. Research prices and use integer operations to generate a budget for your obstacle course. Write a description of how to run your obstacle course, including the change in elevation (based on the starting point) using integers and integer operations. Include your research and description with your model.

P-1C

Step It Out

The U.S. Department of Health and Human Services recommends that people 6 to 17 years old do at least 60 minutes of moderate-to-vigorous physical activity daily. Physical activity promotes healthy bodies and minds and strengthens bones and muscles. Professionals recommend doing a mix of exercises that are aerobic (running, walking, dancing, etc.), muscle-strengthening (climbing trees, tug-of-war, lifting weights, etc.), and bone-strengthening (hopscotch, basketball, tennis, etc.). Bone-strengthening exercises can also be aerobic or muscle-strengthening.

Some people watch workout videos to give them ideas, structure, and guidance as they exercise. In these workout videos, an instructor models each exercise, leading the viewer through an entire workout. Typically, a workout video guides the viewer through several exercise sets, with each set including a specific number of repetitions of each exercise.

Your Project **Film an Exercise Video**

How fast can you walk? Can you walk backward just as fast? Which direction is easier? How big a step can you take?

Film a five-minute exercise video that includes a series of at least 12 exercise sets with at least 15 steps in each set. At least half of your steps must be walking backward. Summarize your workout using all four integer operations. Calculate your location at the end of each set, in number of steps, relative to your starting position (which is 0).

Name _____

How Cold Is Too Cold?
Coldest Places

What are the coldest places on Earth? What are their average temperatures?

Part A Select 2 of the coldest cities and record their average monthly temperatures.

City #1: _____

Temperature Unit (circle one): °C / °F

Month	Avg High	Avg Low	Temp Range
Jan			
Feb			
Mar			
Apr			
May			
Jun			
Jul			
Aug			
Sep			
Oct			
Nov			
Dec			

City #2: _____

Temperature Unit (circle one): °C / °F

Month	Avg High	Avg Low	Temp Range
Jan			
Feb			
Mar			
Apr			
May			
Jun			
Jul			
Aug			
Sep			
Oct			
Nov			
Dec			

Part B Create a double line graph showing the average monthly highs and lows for each country.

Name _____

How Cold Is Too Cold?

Packing for the Cold

How do you survive in the coldest places on Earth?
What equipment and clothing do you need to pack?
If you struggle with your research, try the following phrases to get you started.

- Extreme cold weather clothing
- Extreme cold survival
- Cold weather survival gear list

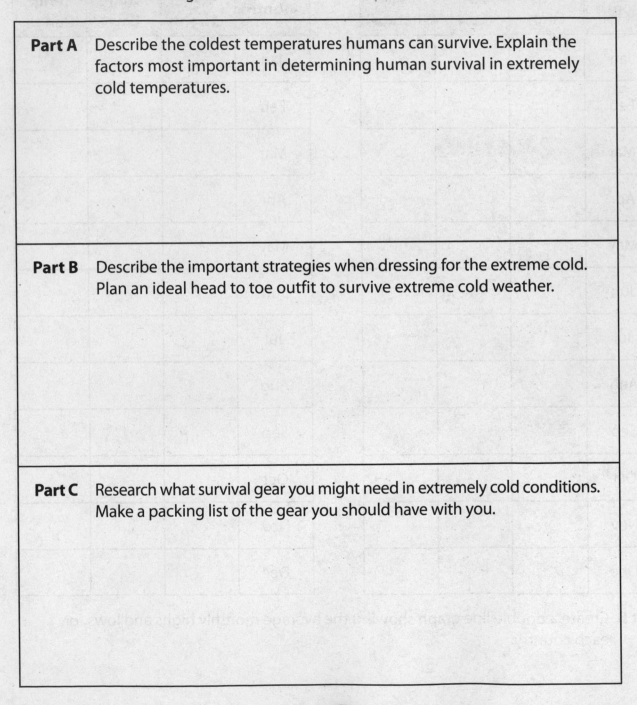

Part A	Describe the coldest temperatures humans can survive. Explain the factors most important in determining human survival in extremely cold temperatures.
Part B	Describe the important strategies when dressing for the extreme cold. Plan an ideal head to toe outfit to survive extreme cold weather.
Part C	Research what survival gear you might need in extremely cold conditions. Make a packing list of the gear you should have with you.

Name _____

Two numbers that are the same distance from 0 on a number line, but in opposite directions, are called opposites. The whole numbers and their opposites make up the set of integers.

Opposites combine to make 0. For example, 3 and −3 are opposites.

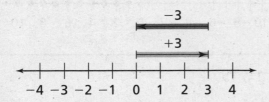

Jacob has saved $50. He spends $15 at the movies. Then, after paying for repairs to his bike, he has $0 remaining. How much did the bike repairs cost?

1. What integer represents Jacob's savings?

2. What integer represents the change in Jacob's savings after he spends money at the movies?

3. The number line represents the change in Jacob's savings after the movies. Use the number line to show Jacob's change in savings after the bike repairs.

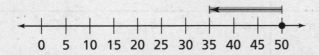

4. What integer represents the change in Jacob's savings due to the bike repairs? What integer represents the cost of the bike repairs?

On the Back!

5. On a winter's morning, the temperature was 0°F. The temperature increased during the daytime. At night, the temperature decreased 6°F and returned to 0°F. What integer represents the temperature change during the daytime? Represent the situation using a number line.

Name _____

Complete the vocabulary chart.

Word or Phrase	Definition	Picture or Example
whole numbers	the counting numbers, plus zero	0, 1, 2, 3, 4, …
positive numbers		$4, 1\frac{1}{2}, 15$
negative numbers	all numbers less than zero; numbers to the left of zero on a number line	
	the set of positive whole numbers, their opposites, and zero	
	the distance from zero on the number line	$\lvert -3 \rvert = 3 \qquad \lvert 5 \rvert = 5$
opposite integers		

Name _____

**Read the problem below. Answer the questions to help you
understand how to use the number line to solve the problem.**

An apartment building has a parking lot with 12 parking spaces for
tenants. At 6 A.M., all 12 spaces were full. At 8 A.M., the number of cars in
the lot had decreased by 4. By 9 A.M., there were no cars left in the lot.
Use the number line to show each change in the number of cars in the
parking lot. What integer represents the change in the number of cars
between 8 A.M. and 9 A.M.?

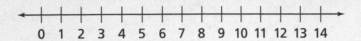

0 1 2 3 4 5 6 7 8 9 10 11 12 13 14

1. Underline the information related to the quantities of cars.

2. What integer is represented by the phrase "decreased by 4"?

3. To represent this situation on the number line, where would you
    start? Explain.

4. Once all of the changes in the number of cars are shown on the
    number line, where will the last arrow end? Explain.

5. Why are there no negative numbers on the number line?

6. Will you use a positive or a negative integer to represent the
    change in the number of cars between 8 A.M. and 9 A.M.? Explain.

Name _____

Raphael's Gym has a climbing wall that starts in the gym's basement, 9 feet beneath the ground level. The wall extends to 21 feet above the ground level.

1. What is the total height of the climbing wall? Represent the situation with a number line. Then, explain how you found your answer.

2. Brennan climbs from the bottom of the wall to the ground level. What integer represents the distance that Brennan climbs? How does this relate to the integer that represents the bottom of the wall?

3. Brennan climbs to a height of 15 feet above ground level. What integer represents Brennan's total change in elevation since he started his climb? Explain using a number line.

4. From his height of 15 feet above ground level, Brennan descends 4 feet, climbs back up 5 feet, and then descends 1 foot. How did Brennan's position change?

5. Brennan's sister Ainsley climbs from the bottom of the wall and stops 4 feet below Brennan. What integer represents Ainsley's height in relation to the ground level? What integer represents Ainsley's climb down to the ground level? Explain using a number line.

Name _____

To write a fraction in decimal form, divide the fraction's numerator by its denominator. The decimal equivalent of a fraction will eventually either terminate or repeat.

Terminating Decimal	**Repeating Decimal**
$\frac{1}{2} = 2\overline{)1.0}^{\,0.5} = 0.5$	$\frac{1}{3} = 3\overline{)1.0000}^{\,0.333\ldots} = 0.\overline{3}$

In a repeating decimal, the repeating digit or digits are shown with a bar.

$$0.111\ldots = 0.\overline{1} \qquad\qquad 0.516363636363\ldots = 0.51\overline{63}$$

Joaquin cut two pieces of paper for an art project. One piece was $\frac{3}{8}$ foot long and the other was $\frac{7}{18}$ foot long. How would you write these fractions in decimal form?

1. Convert each fraction to a decimal number.

$$\frac{3}{8} = 8\overline{)3.000}^{\,0.3\square\square}$$
$$\begin{array}{r} -24 \\ \hline 60 \\ -56 \\ \hline \square\square \\ -40 \\ \hline \square \end{array}$$

$$\frac{7}{18} = 18\overline{)7.000}^{\,0.\square\square\square\ldots}$$
$$\begin{array}{r} -\square\square \\ \hline 1\;6\;0 \\ -\square\square\square \\ \hline 1\;6\;0 \\ -\square\square\square \\ \hline \square\square \end{array}$$

2. Is the decimal equivalent of $\frac{3}{8}$ terminating or repeating?

3. Is the decimal equivalent of $\frac{7}{18}$ terminating or repeating?

4. How do you know when to stop dividing for a terminating decimal? For a repeating decimal?

On the Back!

5. Write the decimal equivalent for $\frac{4}{11}$.

Name _____

**Each section of the graphic organizer contains a vocabulary term
and two examples of the term. Use the list below to complete the
graphic organizer.**

fraction	$6.\overline{3}$	terminating decimal
-9	integer	$-\dfrac{4}{5}$

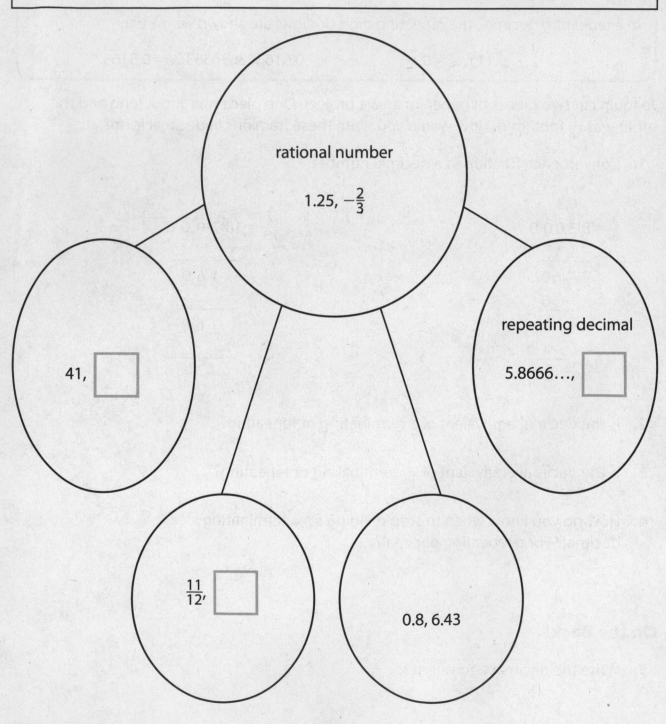

rational number

$1.25, -\dfrac{2}{3}$

repeating decimal

$5.8666\ldots,$ □

41, □

$\dfrac{11}{12},$ □

0.8, 6.43

Name _____

Read the problem below. Then answer the questions to identify the steps for solving the problem.

Mario has been at bat 22 times this baseball season. Of those times at bat, he has hit the ball 15 times. What is the decimal equivalent of the fraction that relates the number of times Mario has been at bat to the number of times he has hit the ball?

1. Underline the information you think might be important to solve this problem.

2. Circle the word that tells what form your answer should be in.

3. Choose the statement that will best help you solve this problem. Explain your choice.

    ☐   All fractions can be written with an equivalent fraction.

    ☐   All rational numbers have a decimal equivalent that either terminates or repeats.

    ☐   Rational numbers can be positive or negative.

4. Complete the table to help you organize the information in this problem.

Number of Hits	Number of At-Bats	Ratio of Hits to At-Bats	Related Division Expression
15			

Name _____

A group of students in a health class track their daily steps to find out how far they walk. The students use different smartphone apps to track their distances. Some apps display distances using decimals, while others use fractions. The table shows the total distances walked by the group of students so far. The battery of Shauna's phone ran out of power before her distance could be recorded.

Distance Walked (miles)				
Jin	**Mariko**	**Clyde**	**Shauna**	**Todd**
$12\frac{7}{8}$	12.6	$12\frac{5}{6}$		12.8

1. Shauna knows that she walked farther than Todd, but not as far as Jin. Use this information to estimate Shauna's distance. Explain your reasoning.

2. The students want to add their individual distances to find the total distance the group walked. Jin suggests writing each distance as a fraction. Why might Jin's suggestion be helpful? Explain.

3. Mariko predicts that the total is between 60 and 65 miles. How might Mariko have determined this?

4. Suppose Shauna walked the same distance as Clyde. What is the total distance the group of students walked, rounded to the nearest tenth?

If you are adding two positive integers, the sum will be positive.

$3 + 5 = 8$

If you are adding two negative integers, the sum will be negative.

$-3 + (-5) = -8$

If you are adding a negative integer and a positive integer, find the difference of the absolute values. The sum will have the sign of the addend with the greater absolute value.

$-3 + 5 = 2$

$|-3| < |5|$, so the sum is positive.

Paula dives into a swimming pool from a diving board 2 feet above the water's surface. She descends to a depth 7 feet below the diving board. How far is Paula from the surface of the water?

1. What integer represents Paula's starting height above the water?

2. What integer represents the total distance Paula descends?

3. Write an addition expression to represent Paula's distance below the water's surface.

4. On the number line below, the arrow represents Paula's starting height above the water. Draw an arrow to represent Paula's dive into the water. Where does your arrow end?

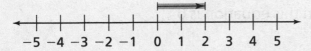

5. At the end of her dive, Paula is ☐ feet below the surface of the water.

On the Back!

6. Yolanda owes her friend $15. She also earns $8 each week in allowance. Write and solve an addition equation to show how the total amount of money that Yolanda has will change if she pays her friend back this week.

Name _____

Use the list below to complete each problem.

4	sum	5	additive inverses	positive integer
14	$|5|$	absolute value	-4	negative integer

1. $-4 + 5$

a. Label the arrows on the number line.

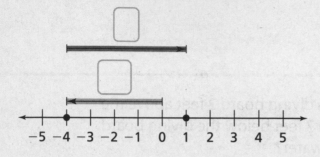

b. The [   ] in this expression is -4.

c. The [   ] in this expression is 5.

d. The absolute value of -4 is [   ].

e. The absolute value of 5 is written as [   ].

2. $14 + (-14) = 0$

a. The [   ] of the two addends in this equation is 0.

b. In this equation, 14 and -14 are [   ] because their sum is 0.

c. The [   ] of -14 or 14 is [   ].

Name _____

**Read the problem below. Answer the questions to help you
understand how to solve the problem.**

Michelle wants to buy a shirt that costs $28. She has saved $20 and has
a store credit that she can apply to the cost of the shirt. A store credit is
shown as a negative balance on the receipt.

Accessories return	$12
Cash refund	$ 0
Credit balance	−$12

Michelle lives in a state that has no sales tax on clothing. Does Michelle
have enough money to buy the shirt?

1. Underline the question that you need to answer.

2. Circle the integers you must add to solve the problem.

3. What are two possible ways that Michelle can solve the problem?
    Explain.

4. Circle the addition expression that represents how much Michelle
    must pay for the shirt after the credit is applied.

    $28 + 12$ $28 + (−12)$ $−28 + 12$ $−28 + (−12)$

5. Why is a store credit represented by a negative number?

Name _____

Tim earns spending money by doing odd jobs for his neighbors.
The table shows how much he is paid for each job.

Job	Money Paid
Mow lawn	$12
Wash car	$9
Walk dog	$7

1. At the beginning of the month, Tim has $50. He mows 2 lawns
   and washes 1 car. Then, he buys two video games that cost $15
   each and a sweatshirt that costs $35. Write an addition equation
   using integers to represent the situation. How much money does
   Tim have left?

2. Tim owes his mother $23. What possible combination of jobs
   could Tim perform to earn enough money to pay back his mother?
   Write an addition equation using integers to represent the
   situation. Will he have money left over?

3. Mr. Jeffries has not paid his bill in 3 weeks. If Tim performed each
   job for Mr. Jeffries once, how much does Mr. Jeffries owe Tim? Write
   an addition equation using integers to represent the situation.
   Represent Mr. Jeffries' balance as an integer.

4. Tim wants to earn $22 to buy a concert ticket. Dr. Martin, one of
   Tim's original customers, still pays Tim's original rates, which are
   $3 less than Tim's current rates for each of his services. Dr. Martin
   asks Tim to mow her lawn and wash both of her cars. Will Tim earn
   enough money to buy the ticket? Explain.

To subtract integers, you can use the additive inverse to write subtraction as an equivalent addition expression. Then follow the rules for addition.

$$-2 - 3 = -2 + (-3)$$
$$\quad\quad = -5$$

$$-2 - (-3) = -2 + 3$$
$$\quad\quad\quad = 1$$

To add integers with the same sign, find the sum of the absolute values and keep the sign.

To add integers with different signs, find the difference of the absolute values and use the sign of the addend with the greater absolute value.

On a cold winter day, the temperature was 1°C below zero. At night, the temperature dropped 4°C. What was the final temperature?

1. What integer represents the daytime temperature?

2. What integer represents the drop in temperature?

3. Write a subtraction expression to represent the final temperature, then write an equivalent addition expression.

4. On the number line below, the arrow represents the starting temperature from zero. Draw an arrow to represent the drop in temperature. At which integer does the arrow end?

5. The final temperature is [ ] °C below zero, or [ ] °C.

On the Back!

6. Marco climbed 2 feet down a ladder. He then climbed down 4 more feet. Write a subtraction equation and an equivalent addition equation to represent this situation. What was the total change in Marco's elevation?

Name _____

Choose the term from the list that *best* represents the item in each box.

sum	positive integers	same signs	absolute value
difference	negative integers	different signs	additive inverse

1. $-1, -2, -3, -4, \ldots$

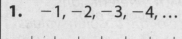

2. $4 - 9 = 4 + (-9)$

3. $-5, 3$

4. $-18 - 5 = -23$
$\uparrow$

5. $|-3| = 3$

6. $2, 5$

7. $-9 + (-5) = -14$
$\uparrow$

8. $1, 2, 3, 4, \ldots$

Use one term from the list above to help you complete the sentence.

9. When subtracting integers, as in $a - b$, you can use the

[   ] to rewrite the subtraction expression

as an equivalent addition expression.

$a - b = a + (-b)$

Name _____

Review the Key Concept from the lesson. Then answer the questions to help you understand how to read a Key Concept.

KEY CONCEPT

When subtracting integers, such as $a - b$, you can use the additive inverse to write subtraction as an equivalent addition expression.

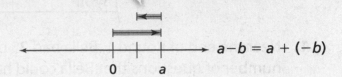

Subtracting b is the same as adding the opposite of b.

$a - b = a + (-b)$

1. What is the focus of this Key Concept box?

2. What do the variables a and b represent?

3. Circle the expression that is not equivalent to the other expressions.

   $a + (-b)$ $a - b$ $b - a$ $(-b) + a$

4. What is true about additive inverses? Select all that apply.

   ☐ The additive inverse of a positive number is negative.

   ☐ The additive inverse of a number is always positive.

   ☐ Additive inverses have a sum of 0.

   ☐ Subtracting is the same as adding the additive inverse.

   ☐ The additive inverse of a number is 0.

Name _____

Enrichment
1-4

Students in a history class are playing a trivia game. A player earns 5 points for each question answered correctly, and loses 3 points for each question answered incorrectly. The table shows the scores of four players at the end of Round 1.

Student	Score
Bella	19
Desmond	− 1
Richie	17
Sybil	− 5

1. Near the end of Round 1, Bella had 25 points. What is a possible number of questions that Bella could have been asked in Round 1? Explain.

2. Desmond answered the last question in Round 1 incorrectly. Write a subtraction equation using integers. What was his score before the last question?

3. Which is greater, the difference between Bella's score and Desmond's score or the difference between Richie's score and Sybil's score? Write subtraction equations using integers to explain.

4. Before Round 2, each player draws a wild card as shown in the table. How many points does each player have to begin Round 2?

Student	Directions on Wild Card	Score Before Round 2
Bella	Subtract − 8 from your score.	
Desmond	Subtract 10 from your score.	
Richie	Subtract 5 from your score.	
Sybil	Subtract − 7 from your score.	

E 1-4

Colin climbs 16 feet down into a tunnel and lands on the tunnel floor. Then he jumps to a platform that is 2 feet above the tunnel floor. Where is Colin located in relation to ground level?

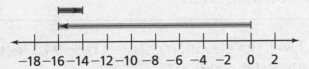

The arrow from 0 to −16 represents Colin's descent into the tunnel. The arrow pointing two units to the right from −16 represents his jump to the platform. Colin is located at −14 feet, or 14 feet below ground level.

The coldest temperature ever recorded on Earth is 135.8°F below 0, recorded in Antarctica on July 21, 1983. The hottest temperature ever recorded on Earth is 134°F, recorded in Death Valley, California, on July 10, 1913. What is the difference between those two temperatures?

1. Is the coldest temperature represented by a positive or negative number?

2. Write a number to represent the coldest temperature.

3. Is the hottest temperature represented by a positive or negative number?

4. Write a number to represent the hottest temperature.

5. Write a subtraction expression to represent the difference of the two temperatures.

6. What is the difference between the two temperatures?

On the Back!

7. Sonya drops a marble while standing on a deck $7\frac{7}{8}$ feet above the ground. The marble falls $4\frac{1}{4}$ feet from Sonya's hand to the deck, and then rolls and falls to the ground. What is the total vertical distance that the marble falls?

Name _____

Use the list below to complete the sentences.

greater	same	number line	less
absolute value	different	additive inverse	

Delia lives in a house that is 113 feet above sea level. Her elevation changes by −94.5 feet when she walks to the harbor. What is the elevation of the harbor?

1. One way to solve the problem is to picture it on a(n)

   [_____].

2. When the signs are the [_____], find the sum of the absolute values and keep the sign.

3. When the signs are [_____], find the difference of the absolute values and keep the sign of the addend that has the greater absolute value.

4. The [_____] of −94.5 is 94.5.

5. Subtracting is the same as adding the [_____], so 113 − 94.5 is the same as 113 + (−94.5).

6. The elevation of the harbor is [_____] than the elevation of Delia's house.

7. The elevation of the harbor is [_____] than the elevation at sea level.

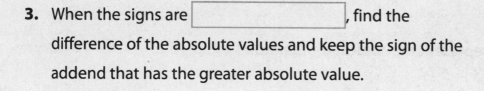

Name _____

Read the word problem below. Then answer the questions to identify the steps for solving the problem.

Maya owes her dad $15.35. The table shows the money that Maya can earn for doing different chores for her family. She mows the grass to earn some money.

Chore	Amount
Return the recyclables	$7.50
Mow the grass	$8.25
Clean the garage	$10.75

How will Maya's balance change after she mows the lawn?

1. Underline the question you need to answer.

2. What will be the units of the answer?

3. Circle the information that you need to solve the problem.

4. Are you given any extra information you do not need? If so, draw a line through the information.

5. What is the sign of each number you will use? Explain. Highlight words that support your reasoning.

Name _____

The table below shows the changes in the value of a company's stock over the past four weeks.

Stock Value			
Week 1	**Week 2**	**Week 3**	**Week 4**
$+9\frac{1}{2}$ points	$+6\frac{5}{8}$ points	$-12\frac{3}{4}$ points	$-8\frac{1}{4}$ points

1. A broker says that during the third week, the company's stock lost all of the points it had gained over the first two weeks. Is this claim correct? Explain.

2. By how many points would the stock value need to change in Week 5 to return to its value before Week 1? Explain.

3. At the beginning of Week 1, the value of the company's stock was $177\frac{3}{8}$ points. An investor tells his broker to sell his shares of stock if the value falls below 170 points at the end of Week 4. Should the broker sell the shares? Explain.

When you multiply two integers with the **same** sign, the product is **positive**.

$$3 \cdot 6 = 18$$
$$-3 \cdot (-6) = 18$$

When you multiply two integers with **different** signs, the product is **negative**.

$$-3 \cdot 6 = -18$$
$$3 \cdot (-6) = -18$$

Riley is training to run in a 5-kilometer road race. She would like to reduce her race time by 15 seconds each month that she trains. The race is in 3 months. What is the total change in time that Riley hopes to achieve?

1. What integer represents the change in race time Riley wants to achieve each month?

2. What integer represents the number of months she will train?

3. Write a multiplication expression that can be used to find the total change in time.

4. Complete the number line to find the product.

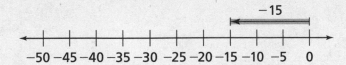

5. What is the total change in race time that Riley hopes to achieve? Explain what this change represents in the situation.

On the Back!

6. Find the product. $-7 \cdot (-5)$

Name _____

Use the list below to complete each sentence.

factor	positive	additive inverses	Commutative Property
product	negative	Distributive Property	Associative Property

1. $-3 \cdot (-12) = -12 \cdot (-3)$

   a. This equation is written using the [_____]
     of Multiplication.

   b. Both factors in this equation are [_____].

   c. The product will be [_____].

2. $-7 \cdot (-8 + 8) = [-7 \cdot (-8)] + [-7 \cdot 8]$

   a. This equation is written using the [_____].

   b. The product of this equation is 0. This is because the sum of the
     [_____], -8 and 8, is equal to 0.

3. $(5 \cdot (-9)) \cdot 6 = 5 \cdot ((-9) \cdot 6)$

   a. This equation is written using the [_____]
     of Multiplication.

   b. One [_____] is negative, while the other two
     are positive.

   c. The [_____] will be negative.

Name _____

**Read the problem below. Then answer the questions to
identify the steps for solving the problem.**

A deep-sea diving bell is a chamber that carries divers deep beneath
the ocean's surface. The diving bell is lowered from the ocean's surface
at a constant rate of 40 feet per minute. What is the diving bell's
change in elevation after 4 minutes?

1. Underline the question you need to answer.

2. Highlight the given information that you will use to solve this
   problem.

3. What units will you use to express the rate at which the bell is
   lowered?

4. What integer represents the change in elevation per minute?
   Circle the word in the problem that tells you the correct sign for
   this integer.

5. Circle the expression that best represents this situation.
   Explain why this expression models the situation.

   $4 \cdot 40$ $\qquad\qquad$ $(-4) \cdot 40$ $\qquad\qquad$ $(-4) \cdot (-40)$ $\qquad\qquad$ $4 \cdot (-40)$

Name _____

Each card in a set has letters on the front side and integers on the reverse. Use the clues given in each problem to discover which numbers are on the reverse sides of the cards.

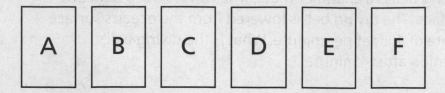

1. The product of A and B is −72.
   Neither A nor B is a multiple of 12.
   The number 12 is not divisible by A or B.
   A is greater than B, but the absolute value of A is less than the absolute value of B. What numbers are on the reverse sides of cards A and B?

2. The product of C and D is −120.
   One number is odd and the other is even.
   The even number is greater than the odd number, but the odd number has a greater absolute value than the even number.
   D is less than C.
   What numbers are on the reverse sides of cards C and D?

3. The product of E and F is 75.
   E is a multiple of F.
   E and F are both negative.
   What numbers are on the reverse sides of cards E and F?

4. Which pair of cards has the greatest possible product?

5. Write your own puzzle. Be sure to use multiplication of integers to create your puzzle.

Name _____

> To multiply rational numbers, you may need to write the numbers in the same form.
>
> Write in equivalent decimal form: $\frac{3}{8} \cdot 0.4 = 0.375 \cdot 0.4$
> $$= 0.15$$
>
> Write in equivalent fraction form: $\frac{1}{7} \cdot 0.65 = \frac{1}{7} \cdot \frac{13}{20}$
> $$= \frac{13}{140}$$
>
> **Remember:** The rules for multiplying integers apply to rational numbers.

The height of a fish tank is 1.1 feet, and the area of the tank's base is $1\frac{1}{4}$ square feet. To find the volume of the tank, multiply the height by the area of the base. What is the volume of the fish tank?

1. Write a multiplication expression with the numbers given to represent the tank's volume.

2. Since one factor is a fraction and the other is a decimal, rewrite one of the factors in an equivalent form. Choose a factor to rewrite and explain your choice.

3. Write a new multiplication expression using your equivalent factor from Item 2 to represent the tank's volume.

4. What is the volume of the fish tank?

On the Back!

5. A hot air balloon is descending at a rate of 6.75 feet per second. What is the change in the balloon's height after $3\frac{1}{3}$ seconds?

Name _____

Match the term on the left with the appropriate example on the right.

decimal expression	$-\frac{3}{5} \cdot \frac{6}{7} = \frac{6}{7} \cdot \left(-\frac{3}{5}\right)$
repeating decimal	$0.\overline{72}$
Commutative Property	$\frac{7}{8} \cdot \left(-\frac{2}{5}\right)$
rational expression	$4.25 \cdot 7.1$

Use each word in the box once to label parts of the equation.

rational number	product	decimal number

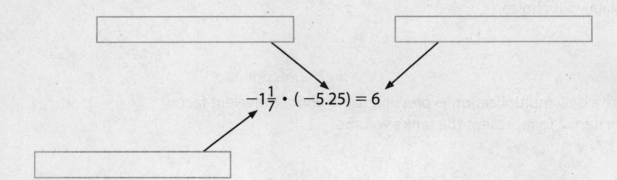

$$-1\frac{1}{7} \cdot (-5.25) = 6$$

Read the problem below. Then answer the questions to identify the steps for solving the problem.

Water is draining from a large swimming pool at a rate of $\frac{7}{8}$ inch per hour. How much will the water level change in $\frac{3}{4}$ hour?

1. Underline the question that you must answer.

2. Circle the important words and numbers that you will use to find the solution.

3. You can simplify the expression $\frac{3}{4} \cdot \left(-\frac{7}{8}\right)$ to find the solution. Explain what each number in the expression means in this context, including its sign. Why does it make sense to multiply the numbers?

4. Which of the following is equivalent to the expression in Exercise 3?

☐ $\frac{3 \cdot (-7)}{8}$

☐ $\frac{3 + (-7)}{4 + 8}$

☐ $\frac{3 \cdot 8}{4 \cdot (-7)}$

☐ $\frac{3 \cdot (-7)}{4 \cdot 8}$

A botanist is studying the development of a bamboo plant.
She started keeping a log of its growth 25 weeks ago.
Since then, the plant has grown an average of $\frac{3}{5}$ inch each
week. Every 5 weeks, she trims $2\frac{1}{2}$ inches off the top of the
bamboo plant. Its current height is $5\frac{3}{4}$ feet.

1. Write an equation to represent the plant's growth since the
   botanist started keeping her log. How much has the plant grown?

2. What is the change in the plant's height from being trimmed?

3. A fellow botanist looks at the log and incorrectly states that the
   bamboo plant is now $27\frac{1}{2}$ inches taller than it was 25 weeks ago.
   What is the correct change in the plant's height? Explain how the
   error was likely made.

4. What was the initial height of the plant when the botanist started
   keeping her log? Show your work.

Name _____

When you divide two integers with the **same** sign, the quotient is **positive**.

$$35 \div 5 = 7$$
$$-35 \div (-5) = 7$$

When you divide two integers with **different** signs, the quotient is **negative**.

$$-35 \div 5 = -7$$
$$35 \div (-5) = -7$$

During one game, a football team lost a total of 12 yards on three consecutive plays. They lost the same number of yards on each play. What was the change in yardage on each play?

1. Write an integer to represent the total change in yardage after the three plays.

2. What is the total number of plays?

3. What is the divisor? What is the dividend?

4. Write a division expression to represent the change in yardage on each play.

5. Will the quotient be positive or negative? Explain.

6. What was the change in yardage on each play?

On the Back!

7. It takes a thermal drill 13 minutes to bore a hole −39 feet from ground level into a glacier. What is the change in depth after one minute?

Name _____

**Use the list below to complete each sentence and provide an
example. Use each term and example only once.**

negative integers	factor	quotient
rational number	divisor	product
$-240 \div 6 = -40$	$-12 \cdot (-8) = 96$	$10 \cdot 3 = 30$
$64 \div 4 = 16$	$\dfrac{66}{-11} = -6$	$-42 \div (-6) = 7$

1. The answer to a division problem is called a ⬚.

   Example: ⬚

2. The quotient in a division equation is a ⬚ in a
   related multiplication equation.

   Example: $30 \div 10 = 3$, so ⬚

3. The quotient of two ⬚ will be positive.

   Example: ⬚

4. The ⬚ of two factors with the same sign will be
   positive.

   Example: ⬚

5. When the ⬚ and the dividend have
   different signs, the quotient will be negative.

   Example: ⬚

6. A ⬚ can be written as the quotient of
   integers with a nonzero divisor.

   Example: ⬚

**Review the Key Concept from the lesson. Then answer the
questions to help you understand how to read a Key Concept.**

> KEY CONCEPT
>
> The rules for dividing integers are related to the rules for
> multiplying integers.
>
> If the signs of the dividend and the divisor
> are the same, the quotient is positive.
>
> $$24 \div 4 = 6 \qquad -24 \div (-4) = 6$$
>
> If the signs of the dividend and the divisor
> are different, the quotient is negative.
>
> $$-15 \div 3 = -5 \qquad 15 \div (-3) = -5$$

1. Underline the expression that represents the quotient of two
   integers at the top of the Key Concept box. Then circle this
   expression written as a rational number.

2. Using this example as a model, how could you write $7 \div 21$ as a
   rational number?

3. Look at the rule and equations on the bottom left of the Key
   Concept box. Explain how the two equations illustrate the rule.

4. Look at the rule and equations on the bottom right. Explain how
   the two equations illustrate the rule.

A water tank contains 150 gallons of water when full. Exactly 24 hours ago, the tank began to leak. There are only 54 gallons remaining in the tank now.

1. What integer represents the change per hour in the number of gallons in the tank? Explain.

2. An alarm will sound when the amount of water in the tank reaches 10 gallons. In how many hours will the alarm begin to sound? Use negative integers to write an equation representing the situation.

3. A technician repairs the leak one hour after the alarm sounds. She then refills the tank at a rate of 3 gallons per minute. How long does it take her to fill the tank halfway? Explain.

> Dividing by a rational number is the same as multiplying by its reciprocal.
>
> The reciprocal of a fraction inverts the numerator and the denominator.
>
> $\frac{3}{4} \div \frac{9}{8} = \frac{3}{4} \cdot \frac{8}{9}$ $\frac{8}{9}$ is the reciprocal of $\frac{9}{8}$.
>
> $\qquad = \frac{2}{3}$

A football team lost a total of $2\frac{1}{2}$ yards in 5 plays. What was the average change in yardage per play?

1. What number represents the total loss in yardage?

2. What is the total number of plays?

3. Write a division expression to represent the average change in yardage per play.

4. Write the numbers in your division expression as fractions.

5. Rewrite the division expression as a multiplication expression.

6. The average change in yardage was ☐ yards per play. This means the team lost ☐ yards per play.

On the Back!

7. A company had a loss of −$1,786.50 over the past 1.5 years. What was the company's average loss per year?

Name _____

Complete the vocabulary chart.

Word or Phrase	Definition	Examples
integers	The integers are the counting numbers, their opposites, and 0.	
rational number	A rational number is any number that can be written in the form $\frac{a}{b}$, where a and b are integers and b does not equal 0.	
complex fraction		$\dfrac{\frac{2}{5}}{-12}$, $\dfrac{\frac{-2}{3}}{\frac{1}{-4}}$
mixed number		
simplify		$\dfrac{-\frac{2}{7}}{1\frac{1}{3}} = -\frac{3}{14}$
reciprocals		

Read the problem below. Then answer the questions to identify the steps for solving the problem.

Marla claims that $\left(-\frac{1}{5}\right) \div \frac{3}{5} = \frac{4}{3} \div (-4)$. Is Marla correct? Explain your reasoning.

1. The equation given in the problem contains two expressions. Underline one of the expressions and circle the other.

2. What do you need to do with these expressions in order to answer the question?

3. Without dividing, can you tell whether the two quotients have the same sign? Explain.

4. To find the quotient when dividing a number by a rational number, you can multiply the dividend by the reciprocal of the divisor. What is the reciprocal of the divisor in each expression?

5. How can you check the solutions after finding each quotient?

In each list of four numbers, there is a dividend, a divisor, a quotient, and a number that does not belong. Write the division problem in the form dividend ÷ divisor = quotient. Cross out the number that does not belong.

1. $-\frac{3}{4}, \frac{2}{3}, -\frac{3}{8}, -\frac{1}{2}$

2. $-\frac{2}{5}, 2, \frac{1}{5}, -\frac{4}{5}$

3. $1\frac{1}{2}, -3\frac{3}{4}, -\frac{2}{3}, -2\frac{1}{2}$

4. $-2.2, -5.5, -0.2, 1.1$

5. $-52, 4, 13, -0.25$

6. $-\frac{3}{5}, \frac{5}{3}, 2\frac{7}{10}, -4\frac{1}{2}$

7. $\frac{7}{30}, -9, -\frac{30}{7}, -2.1$

Bobby and Memphis each have $1\frac{3}{4}$ pounds of pumpkin seeds. They want to share the total amount equally amongst three people. How many pounds of seeds will each person receive?

Step 1: Add. $\quad 1\frac{3}{4} + 1\frac{3}{4} = 3\frac{1}{2}$

Step 2: Divide. $\quad 3\frac{1}{2} \div 3 = \frac{7}{2} \div \frac{3}{1}$

$$= \frac{7}{2} \cdot \frac{1}{3}$$

$$= \frac{7}{6}$$

Each person will receive $1\frac{1}{6}$ pounds of pumpkin seeds.

Rachel will earn $384.61 per week for 8 weeks until college starts. Rachel wants to save $50 per week to buy a bike, and she has budgeted $75 per week for transportation and entertainment expenses. She wants to save the rest of her earnings for college. Will Rachel save at least $2000 for college over the 8 weeks?

1. Multiply Rachel's weekly earnings by the number of weeks to find her total earnings for the summer.

2. Write and solve an equation to represent the change in Rachel's savings when she pays for her bike.

3. Write and solve an equation to represent the change in Rachel's savings after deducting her transportation and entertainment expenses for 8 weeks.

4. Find the sum of the negative changes in Rachel's savings to determine her total expenses before she goes to college.

5. After Rachel pays all of her expenses, how much of her earnings will remain? Explain.

6. Will Rachel save at least $2000 for college? Explain.

On the Back!

7. Manuel has $\frac{5}{8}$ of a pizza to share equally with his brother. What fraction of the original pizza will each person receive?

Name _____

1. **Match each term on the left to the example on the right that**
   best describes it. Use each term exactly once.

terminating decimal	$6\frac{1}{2} - 3\frac{1}{3} = 3\frac{1}{6}$
mixed number	$-\dfrac{\frac{3}{6}}{7}$
rational number	$4\frac{7}{8}$
addition of rational numbers	$-4.5 + 3.6 = -0.9$
subtraction of mixed numbers	$-6.3 \cdot 5 = -31.5$
multiplication of rational numbers	0.071
division of rational numbers	$-7.8 \div 1\frac{1}{2} = -5.2$

2. **Select one of the terms from above to best complete the sentence.**

A [＿＿＿＿＿＿＿] is a number that can be written as a
fraction with a nonzero denominator.

Here are three examples.

$-9\frac{1}{2}, \dfrac{\frac{5}{7}}{8}, 0$

Read the problem below. Then answer the questions to identify the steps for solving the problem.

A rock climber is using a pulley to lower supplies $20\frac{3}{4}$ meters to the bottom of a cliff. The supplies reach the ground in $3\frac{1}{2}$ minutes. If the supplies are lowered at a constant rate, what is the change in elevation per minute?

1. Circle the words in the problem that describe the value you must find.

2. Would you represent the change in elevation with a positive or negative number? Explain how you know.

3. Explain why you can use the expression $\left(-20\frac{3}{4}\right) \div 3\frac{1}{2}$ to find the answer.

4. Circle the terms below that describe the two numbers in the problem.

   mixed fraction   improper fraction   rational number

5. Order the steps to find the quotient in Item 3.

   ☐ Multiply numerators and multiply denominators.

   ☐ Rewrite the mixed numbers as improper fractions.

   ☐ Simplify and give the correct sign.

   ☐ Rewrite division as multiplication by the reciprocal.

Name _____

In science, force is measured in newtons (N). Here on Earth, the force of gravity measures 1 newton. However, gravitational force differs depending on where you are in the universe. The gravitational force on the Moon, for example, measures less than $\frac{1}{5}$ that on Earth.

1. Phobos, one of the moons of Mars, is so small that gravity barely exists there. Gravity on Earth is about 200 times greater than gravity on Phobos. What is the force of gravity on Phobos? Express the answer as a decimal.

2. Suppose a person who jumps on Earth returns to the ground in 0.4 second. On Phobos, the same jumper will take 6.4 minutes to return to the ground. How many times longer would it be on Phobos than on Earth for the jumper to return to the ground? Explain.

3. A jump that reaches a height of 20 centimeters on Earth would reach a height of 340 centimeters on Pluto. The same jump would be $1\frac{3}{17}$ times greater on Phobos than on Pluto. How many times greater is the height of the jump on Phobos than it would be on Earth? Explain.

4. A ball kicked a distance of 20 meters on Earth would travel $2\frac{13}{20}$ times farther on Mars. On Phobos, the ball would travel approximately 716.98 times farther than on Mars. About how many kilometers would the ball travel on Phobos? Explain.

Name _____

Real Numbers

Dear Family,

   Your child is learning to identify and work with different types of real numbers, such as integers, rational numbers, and irrational numbers. This will include comparing real numbers, evaluating square roots and cube roots, simplifying expressions involving exponents, and working with numbers written in scientific notation.
   Here is an activity to help your child understand positive and negative exponents.

What's the Greatest?

Materials: A standard deck of playing cards with the face cards removed

Step 1   Shuffle the cards and place four cards face up. Red cards represent negative numbers and black cards represent positive numbers. For example, the cards shown below represent 5, −6, 2, and −3.

$$\boxed{5} \quad \boxed{6} \quad \boxed{2} \quad \boxed{3}$$

Step 2   Working with your child, arrange the given numbers to form an expression containing exponents. For example, using the cards above, you could write $5^{-3} + (-6)^2$. Then simplify the expression with your child.

$$5^{-3} + (-6)^2 = \frac{1}{5 \cdot 5 \cdot 5} + (-6) \cdot (-6)$$
$$= \frac{1}{125} + 36 = 36\frac{1}{125}.$$

Challenge yourselves to find an exponential expression with the greatest possible value using these numbers.

Observe Your Child

Focus on Mathematical Practices
Model with mathematics

Help your child become proficient with this Mathematical Practice. Find a fact or statement that contains a number written in scientific notation, such as "The Andromeda Galaxy is 2.5×10^6 light years away." Help your child understand that writing 10^6 as 1,000,000 and performing the multiplication shows that 2.5×10^6 is equivalent to 2,500,000.

Nombre _____

Números reales

Estimada familia:

Su hijo o hija está aprendiendo a identificar y trabajar con diferentes tipos de números reales, como los enteros, números racionales y números irracionales. Esta tarea incluirá comparar números reales, evaluar raíces cuadradas y raíces cúbicas, simplificar expresiones que contengan exponentes y trabajar con números escritos en notación científica.

Esta es una actividad que ayudará a su hijo o hija a entender los exponentes positivos y negativos.

¿Cuál es el mayor?

Materiales: Una baraja de cartas común, sin las cartas con figuras

Paso 1 Mezcle las cartas y coloque cuatro boca arriba. Las cartas rojas representan números negativos y las cartas negras representan números positivos. Por ejemplo, las cartas que se muestran a continuación representan 5, −6, 2 y −3.

Paso 2 Con su hijo o hija, ordenen los números dados para formar una expresión que contenga exponentes. Por ejemplo, con las cartas que se muestran arriba, podrían escribir la expresión $5^{-3} + (-6)^2$. Luego, simplifiquen la expresión.

$$5^{-3} + (-6)^2 = \frac{1}{5 \cdot 5 \cdot 5} + (-6) \cdot (-6)$$
$$= \frac{1}{125} + 36 = 36\frac{1}{125}.$$

Intenten usar esos números para hallar una expresión exponencial con el mayor valor posible.

Observe a su hijo o hija

Enfoque en las Prácticas matemáticas
Representar con modelos matemáticos.

Ayude a su hijo o hija a adquirir competencia en esta Práctica matemática. Halle una operación o un enunciado que contenga un número escrito en notación científica, como "La galaxia Andrómeda se encuentra a 2.5×10^6 años luz de distancia". Ayude a su hijo o hija a entender que escribir 10^6 como 1,000,000 y hacer la multiplicación muestra que 2.5×10^6 es equivalente a 2,500,000.

Name _____

Powerful Poetry

People have written poetry as a way to
express feelings and ideas for thousands
of years. Most poems combine rhythm
and rhyme into intriguing phrases and
thoughts. The *content* of a poem is its
subject matter. The *form* of a poem
refers to the number of lines or groups
of lines, called *stanzas*; its *meter*, or
pattern of stressed and unstressed
syllables; and its rhyme pattern.

The cold wind wanders
Singing birds look
to the south
Winter is nearing

There are many different types of
poetry. Shakespeare and Milton each
wrote many sonnets. A sonnet has
14 lines that follow one of three
possible rhyme patterns. The Japanese
poetry of *haiku* originated in the
9th century. This non-rhyming poetry
style uses only 17 syllables in three lines—
5 syllables, 7 syllables, and 5 syllables. Free verse
poetry has neither rhyme nor a regular meter.

Your Project **Write a Poem**

Think about the different types of poems that you have read. What were
the messages of the poems? Did the poems have noticeable patterns of
stressed and unstressed syllables? Did some of the words in the poems
rhyme? Why do you think you remember some poems better than
others? Have you ever read a poem about math?

Write your own math poem. The content of your poem should reflect
what you know about the properties of integer exponents or scientific
notation. Challenge yourself by playing with the poem's form —use a fun
rhythm, use a pattern of syllables, or make it rhyme! Then make a video
of yourself reciting your poem.

Tiny Houses

Some people are choosing to live more simply. Reasons for this choice include environmental concerns, financial independence, or a desire for more time and freedom. A tiny house is one way to live a simpler life.

A tiny house is a residential building with less than 500 square feet of floor space. By comparison, in the United States, the average size of a traditional home built in 2018 was more than 2,400 square feet.

People who live in tiny houses need to be creative in their use of space. Some tiny houses have multi-purpose furniture, while others have loft spaces and multi-purpose areas. It may be challenging to find storage space in a tiny house, and solutions range from bins built in under the stairs to closets that slide into walls.

Your Project **Design a Tiny House**

Design a tiny house in the shape of a cube. All walls, floors, windows, and doors must be squares. Your tiny house should have less than 500 square feet of floor space. Make a model of your tiny house.

Write a report that includes the dimensions, volume, and floor area of both the model and the actual tiny house (if you were to build it). Include the diagonal lengths of all floors, walls, windows, and doors.

Traveling Through Space

In many science-fiction novels, people travel through space almost as fast as the speed of light. At the blink of an eye, they move not only within the solar system but between stars and out to distant galaxies. Although this is fiction today, maybe someday spacecrafts will travel faster than the speed of light or through hyperspace, an area outside of time and speed restrictions.

Whatever way humans choose to travel in the future, entrepreneurs will be sure to market new and exciting vacations to the stars. Imagine spending the holidays visiting Jupiter's moons or tracing the path of the stars in the Big Dipper.

· ·

Your Project **Plan a Tour of the Milky Way**

Suppose you are a travel agent planning a group tour of the Milky Way. Your travel agency will base the cost of the trip on the miles traveled during the tour. Put together a slideshow describing a themed itinerary of at least five celestial destinations. Your slideshow should include imagined highlights of the locales, and, in scientific notation, the actual distances traveled between destinations.

Name _____

Folk Stories

Folk stories describe adventures and tell of changes over time. These stories are passed down from one generation to the next. Over time, the tales are embellished, facts merge with fiction, and details change or are forgotten. Eventually, it can be difficult to remember what is true and what is imaginary. Such is the case with the history of the number *zero*.

Zero does more than indicate that 7,000 is greater than 7. Zero is the point that connects negative numbers to positive numbers. Zero is the average of any number and its opposite. Zero is *nothing*, but it is more than nothing.

Your Project **Tell a Folk Story**

Think about how telling stories plays a role in your family's culture. Tell a folk story about the history of irrational numbers. Research what is known about irrational numbers, their development, and why they are important. Either write your folk story down or record yourself telling your tale.

Name _____

Going, Going, Gone?
Sustaining Natural Resources

What	Choose a natural resource.
Uses	Describe the uses for your resource.
How Much	How much of it exists in the world? What rate is the resource being depleted?
Impacts	What factors impact the rate that the resource is being depleted? What are the positive impacts of using this resource? What are the negative impacts of using this resource?
Write	Write a story that illustrates the sustainability of your resource.

Name _____

Going, Going, Gone?

Calculating Natural Resource Depletion

Sample Mineral	Your Mineral
Starting Quantity (Year)	
300 million tons (2005)	
Annual Depletion Rate	
1.333%	
Table Make a table that shows the mineral's depletion over time.	
Graph Draw a graph that shows the mineral's depletion over time.	
Solution Find the remaining quantity of the mineral 40 years later.	

Name _____

How can you write $0.\overline{72}$ as a fraction?

Set the decimal number equal to x.

Multiply each side by a power of 10 to get repeating numbers to the left of the decimal point.

Subtract the equations to eliminate the repeating decimals.

Solve for x.

Let $x = 0.\overline{72}$.

$100x = 72.\overline{72}$

$100x - x = 72.\overline{72} - 0.\overline{72}$

$99x = 72$

$\dfrac{99x}{99} = \dfrac{72}{99}$

$x = \dfrac{8}{11}$

In yesterday's basketball game, Raul made $77.\overline{7}\%$ of his shots. What fraction of his shots did he make?

1. How would you write $77.\overline{7}\%$ as a decimal? Set that decimal equal to x. What digit or digits repeat?

2. Multiply each side of the equation by a power of 10 to get the repeating digit(s) to the left of the decimal point. Since you only need to move one place, multiply each side by 10.

3. Subtract the equation in Exercise 1 from the equation in Exercise 2. Then simplify.

4. Divide each side of the equation by 9 to solve for x. What fraction is equal to x? Show your work.

5. What fraction of Raul's shots did he make?

On the Back!

6. This season, Jenny's lacrosse team had a winning percentage of $0.8\overline{3}$. What fraction of their games did Jenny's team win?

Name _____

Choose the term from the list that *best* represents the item in each box.

equivalent	fraction	mixed number	nonrepeating digit
power of 10	repeating decimal	repeating digits	terminating decimal

1. $4\frac{3}{11}$	**2.** $0.\overline{6}$
3. $0.\overline{45} \cdot 100 = 45.\overline{45}$	**4.** $2.8333\ldots$
5. $2.1818\mathbf{18}\ldots$	**6.** $0.555\ldots = \frac{5}{9}$
7. $\frac{5}{6}$	**8.** 0.625

Read the problem below. Then answer the questions to help you understand the problem.

As part of her science project, Malia plans to compare the weights of several different objects on Earth to their weights on Mars.

Object	Weight on Earth	Weight on Mars
Camera	27 oz	
Laptop	40 oz	
USB microscope	15 oz	

To find the weights on Mars, she must multiply each weight on Earth by the decimal 0.376666.... . What fraction could Malia use to make the same calculation?

1. Underline the question that you need to answer.

2. Circle the number that you need to convert to a fraction.

3. How can you rewrite the repeating decimal using bar notation? Explain.

4. Circle the equation you could use to write the repeating decimal as a fraction.

   $x = 0.37\overline{6}$ $x = 3.7\overline{6}$ $x = 37.\overline{6}$ $x = 37.\overline{6}$

5. After you set up the equation, what is the next step in converting the repeating decimal to a fraction?

6. How can you check that your answer is correct?

Name _____

Consider the decimal 0.27227222722227... .

1. Is the decimal number rational or irrational? Explain.

2. Assuming the pattern continues, what are the next 6 digits in the decimal number?

3. How many times will the digit 2 appear in total before the sixth 7 in the decimal number?

4. The digit 7 appears in the second decimal place, the fifth decimal place, and the ninth decimal place. What are the next three places in which the digit 7 appears? Describe the pattern.

5. Write your own decimal that is nonterminating and nonrepeating, using a different type of pattern than the one above. Describe the pattern.

E 2-1

Name _____

Rational Numbers	**Irrational Numbers**
Any number that can be written as a ratio of two nonzero integers is a rational number.	Numbers that are not rational are called irrational.
Decimal expansions of rational numbers either terminate or repeat.	The decimal expansion of an irrational number does not terminate or repeat.
All integers are rational numbers.	Square roots of nonperfect squares are irrational numbers.
Examples: -235 $\frac{3}{4}$ $0.9\overline{4}$	Examples: $4.121121112...$ π $\sqrt{8}$

For each square below, is the side length rational or irrational?

$A = 81$ cm^2 $A = 89$ cm^2

1. What is the formula for the area of a square?

2. If you know the area of a square, how can you find its side length?

3. Write the side length of each square as a square root.

4. Is each side length rational or irrational? Explain.

On the Back!

5. Vidal has a screw that measures $\frac{1}{7}$ inch. Is $\frac{1}{7}$ a rational number or an irrational number? Explain.

Complete the vocabulary chart. Include two examples of each term.

Word or Phrase	Definition	Examples
rational number		$46, -\frac{3}{7}$
irrational number	An irrational number is any number that cannot be written in the form $\frac{a}{b}$, where a and b are integers and $b \neq 0$.	
square root		$\sqrt{4} = 2$ because $2^2 = 4$; $\sqrt{36} = 6$ because $6^2 = 36$.
perfect square		9 because $3^2 = 9$; 25 because $5^2 = 25$.
real number	A real number is a number that is a rational or irrational number.	

Name _____

Read the Key Concept from the lesson. Then use the Venn diagram to answer the questions below.

KEY CONCEPT

KEY CONCEPT

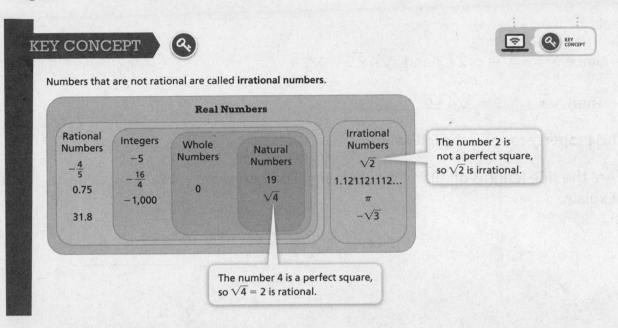

Numbers that are not rational are called **irrational numbers**.

Real Numbers

Rational Numbers
$-\dfrac{4}{5}$
0.75
31.8

Integers
-5
$-\dfrac{16}{4}$
$-1,000$

Whole Numbers
0

Natural Numbers
19
$\sqrt{4}$

Irrational Numbers
$\sqrt{2}$
1.121121112...
π
$-\sqrt{3}$

The number 2 is not a perfect square, so $\sqrt{2}$ is irrational.

The number 4 is a perfect square, so $\sqrt{4} = 2$ is rational.

1. What are the ways that 0 can be classified? Which is most specific?

2. What are all the sets of numbers that are contained within the rational numbers?

3. Circle the rational numbers in the Venn diagram that are not integers. How are these numbers shown in the Venn diagram?

4. How does the Venn diagram show that every irrational number is also a real number?

Name _____

The Product Property of Square Roots states that for any positive numbers a and b, $\sqrt{a} \cdot \sqrt{b} = \sqrt{a \cdot b}$.

Example

Since $\sqrt{4} \cdot \sqrt{9} = 2 \cdot 3$ and $\sqrt{4 \cdot 9} = \sqrt{36}$
$\qquad\qquad\qquad = 6 \qquad\qquad\qquad\quad = 6$
Then $\sqrt{4} \cdot \sqrt{9} = \sqrt{4 \cdot 9}$.

Use this Property to solve the following problems.

1. Are the side lengths of this rectangle rational or irrational? Explain.

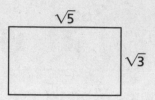

2. Is the area of the rectangle in Problem 1 rational or irrational? Explain.

3. Is it possible for a rectangle to have irrational side lengths and a rational area? If so, give an example. If not, explain.

4. Is it possible for a rectangle to have rational side lengths and an irrational area? If so, give an example. If not, explain.

Between which two whole numbers is $\sqrt{19}$?

$16 < 19 < 25$ Order 19 between two consecutive perfect squares.

$\sqrt{16} < \sqrt{19} < \sqrt{25}$ Take the square root of each number.

$4 < \sqrt{19} < 5$ $\sqrt{16} = 4$ and $\sqrt{25} = 5$.

$\sqrt{19}$ is closer to 4 than it is to 5 since 19 is closer to 16 than it is to 25.

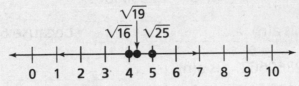

Cameron wants the longest skateboard sticker he can find. An online shop has stickers that are $9\frac{2}{5}$ inches, $9.\overline{35}$ inches, and $\sqrt{80}$ inches long. What is the length of the longest sticker?

1. Write $9\frac{2}{5}$ in decimal form.

2. Approximate $\sqrt{80}$ by using perfect squares. 80 is between which two perfect squares?

   What are the square roots of those two perfect squares?

   What is the approximate value of $\sqrt{80}$?

3. Write the lengths of the bumper stickers in order from least to greatest.

4. What is the length of the longest bumper sticker?

On the Back!

5. Ephraim's car is $\sqrt{120}$ feet long. Hadley's car is 15 feet long. Whose car is longer? Explain.

Name _____

Use the bank below to complete each sentence. You may use terms more than once.

rational number	greater than	approximation	square root
perfect square	irrational number	less than	order

1. $\sqrt{36} = 6$ $\qquad$ $\sqrt{5} = 2.2360667\ldots$

   a. The number 36 is a(n) $\boxed{}$ because $6 \times 6 = 36$.

   b. The number $2.2360667\ldots$ is a(n) $\boxed{}$
   because it cannot be written as a fraction.

   c. To compare $\sqrt{36}$ and $\sqrt{5}$, you can write $\sqrt{36}$ is
   $\boxed{}$ $\sqrt{5}$.

2. $\sqrt{81} > \sqrt{64} > \sqrt{44}$

   a. The value of $\sqrt{64}$ is $\boxed{}$ $\sqrt{81}$ and $\boxed{}$
   $\sqrt{44}$.

   b. You know the number 44 is not a(n) $\boxed{}$,
   because no integer multiplied by itself equals 44.

   c. Rounded to the nearest tenth, a(n) $\boxed{}$
   for $\sqrt{44}$ is 6.6.

3. $\sqrt{25} = 5$ $\qquad$ $\sqrt{16} = 4$ $\qquad$ $\pi \approx 3.14$

   a. The $\boxed{}$ of 25 equals 5.

   b. The $\boxed{}$ of 16 equals 4.

   c. Rounded to the nearest hundredth, a(n) $\boxed{}$
   for π is 3.14.

   d. Compare and $\boxed{}$ the numbers from least to greatest;
   π is $\boxed{}$ $\sqrt{16}$, which is $\boxed{}$ $\sqrt{25}$.

Read the problem below. Then answer the questions to help you understand the problem.

Tianna is designing a quilt block. She will cut from two different sizes of rectangular fabric scraps to create a spiral pattern. Which rectangular scrap has the longer diagonal?

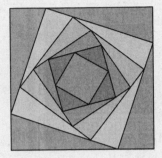
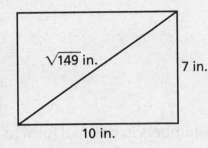
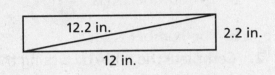

1. What does the problem ask you to do?

2. Circle the information given in the diagrams.

3. Do you need all of the information in the diagrams to solve the problem? If so, explain. If not, cross out the numbers that you will not use.

4. What do you need to do before you can solve the problem?

5. Can you solve the problem just by measuring the lengths in the diagrams? Explain.

Name _____

Four rational approximations of the irrational number $\sqrt{62}$ are $7\frac{17}{20}$, $7.8\overline{7}$, 7.87, and 7.9. Determine which approximation is closest to $\sqrt{62}$ without going over by answering the questions below.

1. Estimate $\sqrt{62}$ using perfect squares. Between which two whole numbers is $\sqrt{62}$ located? Narrow the interval by estimating $\sqrt{62}$ to the nearest tenth.

2. Complete the table by writing the numbers in decimal form to the nearest hundredth.

Estimate	Decimal Form
$7\frac{17}{20}$	
$7.8\overline{7}$	
7.87	

3. Label the tick marks on the number line and plot the three estimates from the table above.

7.80   7.90

4. Which estimate is closest to $\sqrt{62}$ without going over? Explain. Then plot $\sqrt{62}$ on the number line.

Name _____

A square root is one of
two equal factors of a number.

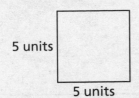

5 units

5 units

$5 \times 5 = 25$, so $\sqrt{25} = 5$.

A cube root is one of
three equal factors of a number.

5 units

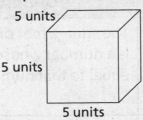

5 units

5 units

$5 \times 5 \times 5 = 125$, so $\sqrt[3]{125} = 5$.

Alistair has a cube-shaped box that has a volume of 216 cubic inches. What is the edge length of Alistair's box?

1. What is the formula for the volume of a cube?

2. If you know the volume of a cube, how do you find its edge length?

3. How would you write the edge length of Alistair's box using a cube root?

4. Fill in the boxes to find the cube root.

$$\sqrt[3]{216} = \sqrt[3]{6 \cdot \square \cdot \square}$$
$$= \sqrt[3]{\square^3}$$
$$= \square$$

5. What is the edge length of Alistair's box?

On the Back!

6. Sian's room is in the shape of a square. Its area is 121 square feet. How long is one side of Sian's room?

Name _____

Complete the vocabulary chart.

Term	Definition	Example
square root	The square root of a number is a number whose square is equal to that number.	
perfect square		Since $7^2 = 49$, 49 is a perfect square.
cube root		Since $\sqrt[3]{8} = 2$, 2 is the cube root of 8.
perfect cube	A perfect cube is a number that is the cube of an integer.	

Complete each sentence using the terms from the vocabulary chart above. You may use each term more than once.

1. The number 25 is a [_____]. The [_____] of 25 equals 5.

2. The number 216 is a [_____]. The [_____] of 216 equals 6.

3. The number 64 is a [_____] and a [_____].

   Its [_____] is 8 and its [_____] is 4.

V 2-4

Name _____

**Read the problem below. Then answer the questions to
help you understand the problem.**

Manuel rented a cube-shaped storage unit with the volume shown
below. What is the height of the storage unit?

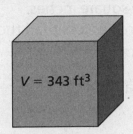

$V = 343 \text{ ft}^3$

1. Underline the question that you need to answer.

2. Circle the important information you are given in the diagram.

3. What will be the units of your answer? How do you know?

4. What necessary information do you need to know about a cube to
    solve the problem?

5. How can you use the given information to find the edge length?

Name _____

Paul has three cube-shaped boxes. Each box is a different size and they are stacked from the largest to the smallest. Some information about the boxes is given below.

- The combined volume of the three boxes is 1,197 cubic inches.
- The area of one face of the medium box is 49 square inches.
- The volume of the smallest box is 218 cubic inches less than the volume of the medium box.

1. What is the volume of the medium box? Explain.

2. What is the area of one face of the smallest box? Explain.

3. What is the edge length of the largest box? Explain.

4. What is the total height of the stack of boxes? How do you know?

5. Paul wants to gift wrap the boxes. He has 1,000 in.² of wrapping paper. Does Paul have enough paper to wrap all three boxes? Explain.

Name _____

Sandi is tiling her bathroom counter. Each square tile has an area of 9 square inches. How many tiles will fit along a side of the counter that measures 15 inches?

Find the side length of each tile.

$A = s^2$ — Use the formula for area of a square.

$9 = s^2$ — Substitute 9 for A.

$\sqrt{9} = \sqrt{s^2}$ — Take the square root of each side.

$\pm 3 = s$ — Simplify.

Since length is positive, each side length of the tile is 3 inches. So, the number of tiles that will fit along a 15-inch side of the counter is $15 \div 3 = 5$, or 5 tiles.

Carlo is building a wooden box that is shaped like a cube. He wants the box to have a volume of 64 cubic inches. How many square inches of wood does Carlo need to build the box?

$V = 64$ in.^{3}

1. What is the length of one edge of the box?

2. What is the area of one face of the box?

3. What is the total area of all faces of the box?

4. How much wood does Carlo need to build his box?

On the Back!

5. Marjorie has a square tabletop whose area is 36 square feet. What is the tabletop's perimeter?

Name _____

Use the bank below to complete each sentence.

square root	perfect square	length	area	positive
cube root	perfect cube	edge	volume	negative

1. $V = s^3$

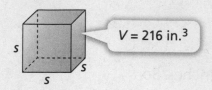

$V = 216$ in.^{3}

a. The ⬚ of this cube is 216 cubic inches.

b. The ⬚ of 216 is 6 because $6 \times 6 \times 6 = 216$.

c. The number 216 is a ⬚ because $6^3 = 216$.

d. The ⬚ of each ⬚ of the cube is 6 inches.

e. The ⬚ of one face of the cube is 36 square inches.

2. If $x^2 = 121$, what is $\sqrt{x^2}$?

a. Since $11^2 = 121$, the number 121 is a ⬚.

b. The number 11 is a ⬚ of 121, as is its opposite -11.

c. The square root of a number can be either ⬚ or ⬚.

**Read the problem below. Then answer the questions to
help you understand the problem.**

Carla's vet suggested that her new puppy have at least 64 square feet
of exercise space. Carla plans to build an enclosed, square exercise pen
in her back yard. How much fencing will she need for this exercise pen?

$A = 64$ square feet

1. Circle the word in the problem that describes the shape of the
   exercise pen. Highlight the area of the pen.

2. What do you need to find to determine how much fencing is
   needed?

3. What value do you need to find first in order to calculate the
   perimeter? Explain how this value is found.

4. Can the length of one side be a negative number? Explain.

5. If you find the length of one side, have you answered the
   question? Explain.

Name _____

Talia is making a stained glass window.
She arranges small, medium, and large squares
of glass in the pattern shown below.

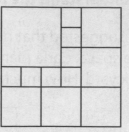

1. The area of each small square is 16 square centimeters.
   What is the side length of the window? Explain.

2. Talia has a square piece of blue glass with an area of 320 square
   centimeters. What is the greatest number of medium squares that
   Talia can cut from this piece? Explain.

3. After completing the window, Talia places it in a frame. The total
   area of the window with the frame is 900 square centimeters.
   How wide is the frame? Explain.

4. Talia has a cube-shaped box with a volume of 17,576 cubic
   centimeters. Will one of her framed windows fit flat along the
   bottom of this box? Explain.

Name _____

Product of Powers Property: When multiplying powers with the same base, add the exponents while keeping the base the same.

$$3^4 \times 3^3 = 3^{4+3}$$
$$= 3^7$$

Quotient of Powers Property: When dividing powers with the same base, subtract the exponents while keeping the base the same.

$$3^4 \div 3^3 = 3^{4-3}$$
$$= 3^1$$

Part A Use the properties of exponents to write an equivalent expression for $2^3 \times 2^8$.

1. What is the common base?

2. What is the sum of the exponents?

3. What power is equivalent to the multiplication expression?

Part B Use the properties of exponents to write an equivalent expression for $5^9 \div 5^6$.

4. What is the common base?

5. What is the difference of the exponents?

6. What power is equivalent to the division expression?

On the Back!

7. Write equivalent expressions using the properties of exponents.

   a. $4^4 \div 4^2$ b. $7^4 \times 7^8$

Name _____

Complete the vocabulary chart.

Property	Definition	Example
Product of Powers Property		$3^2 \cdot 3^4 = 3^6$
Power of a Power Property	When a power is raised to another power, multiply the exponents.	
Power of Products Property		$2^3 \cdot 5^3 = (2 \cdot 5)^3 = 10^3$
Quotient of Powers Property	When two numbers have the same base, divide the numbers by keeping the common base and subtracting the exponents.	

Match each property with an example. Assume variables are nonzero.

Power of a Power Property	$a^m \div a^n = a^{m-n}$
Power of Products Property	$a^n \cdot b^n = (a \cdot b)^n$
Product of Powers Property	$(a^m)^n = a^{mn}$
Quotient of Powers Property	$a^m \cdot a^n = a^{m+n}$

Name _____

**Read the problem below. Then answer the questions to
help you understand the problem.**

Use the properties of exponents to write an equivalent expression for $\frac{7^{10}}{7^9}$.

1. What does *equivalent expression* mean?

2. In the given expression, what operation does the fraction bar
   between 7^{10} and 7^9 represent?

3. Circle the property you can use to write an expression equivalent to $\frac{7^{10}}{7^9}$.

   Product of Powers Property   Power of a Power Property

   Power of Products Property   Quotient of Powers Property

4. In the expression $\frac{7^{10}}{7^9}$, what number(s) represent a base?

5. What number(s) represent an exponent?

6. How can using the properties of exponents make it easier to solve
   this problem?

Name _____

The area formulas for several shapes are shown below.

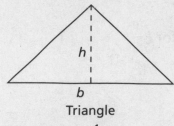 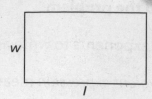

Triangle
$A = \frac{1}{2}bh$

Circle
$A = \pi r^2$

Rectangle
$A = lw$

1. A triangle has a base of 2^3 units and a height of 2^4 units. What is the area of the triangle? Write your answer as a power of 2.

2. A rectangle has a length of 5^3 units and a width of 5^2 units. What is the area of the rectangle? Write your answer as a power of 5.

3. A circle has a radius of 5^4 units. What is the area of the circle? Write your answer using a power of 5.

4. A triangle has a base of 3^2 units and a height of 2^3 units. Write two equivalent expressions for the triangle's area using exponents.

5. A rectangle has a length of x^2 units and a width of y^5 units. A triangle has a base of y^5 units and a height of x^4 units. Jenna mistakenly says that the areas of the rectangle and triangle are equal. What was Jenna's likely error?

Name _____

Zero Exponent Property: For any nonzero number a, $a^0 = 1$.

$$4^0 = 1$$

Negative Exponent Property: For any nonzero number a and integer n, $a^{-n} = \frac{1}{a^n}$.

$$4^{-2} = \frac{1}{4^2} = \frac{1}{16}$$

Answer the questions to complete the table.

2^2	2^1	2^0	2^{-1}	2^{-2}
4				

1. What is the value of any number raised to the power of 1? Write the value of 2^1 in the table.

2. What rule would you use to find the value of 2^0? Write this value in the table.

3. What rule would you use to find the value of 2^{-1}? Write this value in the table.

4. What rule would you use to find the value of 2^{-2}? Write this value in the table.

On the Back!

5. Make a table like the one above that shows the values of 5^2, 5^1, 5^0, 5^{-1}, and 5^{-2}.

Name _____

Complete the sentences using the bank below.

Negative Exponent Property	zero	positive
Zero Exponent Property	expression	negative

1. According to the [   ], any nonzero number with an exponent of [   ] is equal to 1.

2. According to the [   ], the [   ] a^{-n} can be rewritten as $\frac{1}{a^n}$, when a and $n \neq 0$.

3. An exponent changes from [   ] to [   ] when it moves from the numerator to the denominator.

For each equation, write *Zero Exponent Property* or *Negative Exponent Property*.

$5^{-3} = \frac{1}{125}$	$82^0 = 1$
$-(6^0) = -1$	$7^{-2} = \frac{1}{49}$

Name _____

**Read the Key Concept from the lesson. Then answer the
questions to help you understand the Key Concept.**

KEY CONCEPT

Use these additional properties when simplifying or generating equivalent
expressions with exponents (when a and $n \neq 0$).

Zero Exponent Property	Negative Exponent Property
$a^0 = 1$	$a^{-n} = \dfrac{1}{a^n}$

1. Why is the property on the left called the Zero Exponent Property?

2. What does the Zero Exponent Property tell you about a number
   raised to the power of 0?

3. Can you use the Zero Exponent Property to find the value of 0^0?
   Explain.

4. In the expression 4^{-3}, underline the number that corresponds to
   a in the Negative Exponent Property and circle the number that
   corresponds to n. What does the Negative Exponent Property tell
   you about the expression 4^{-3}?

5. The Negative Exponent Property cannot be applied to what base?
   Why do you think this base is not included?

Name _____

Each student in a math class was given a different exponential expression. Three students' expressions are shown in the table below. Assume all variables are nonzero.

Student	Expression	Expression with Positive Exponents	Value for $a = 2$, $b = -1$, $c = 3$
Josie	$\dfrac{a^{-3}b^2}{5^{-1}c^0}$		
Maria	$\dfrac{5a^3c^1}{b^{-2}}$		
Emmanuel	$\dfrac{5}{a^3b^{-2}c^0}$		

1. Rewrite each expression using only positive exponents. Write your answers in the third column of the table.

2. Are any of the expressions equivalent? If yes, which ones?

3. Evaluate each expression for $a = 2$, $b = -1$, and $c = 3$. Write your answers in the fourth column of the table.

4. Does c^0 affect the value of Josie's and Emmanuel's expressions for nonzero values for a, b, and c? Explain.

5. Find values for a, b, and c for which the value of Maria's expression is less than 1.

Name _____

Use a single digit times a power of 10 to estimate the number 602,056,118.

Step 1 Round 602,056,118 to its greatest place value.

600,000,000

Step 2 Write 600,000,000 as a single digit times a power of 10 by counting the number of zeros to determine the power of 10.

$600000000. \rightarrow 6 \times 10^8$
8 7 6 5 4 3 2 1

The average distance from Earth to the Moon is 384,403 kilometers. What is this estimated distance written as a single digit times a power of 10?

1. Underline the number representing the distance in the problem. Then circle the digit to the right of the digit with the greatest place value.

2. When rounding this number to its greatest place value, will you round up or down? Explain.

3. What is the distance from Earth to the Moon rounded to its greatest place value?

4. Count the zeros in the estimated number to determine the power of 10. What is the power of 10?

5. What is the estimated distance from Earth to the Moon written as a single digit times a power of 10?

On the Back!

6. Light travels a distance of one mile in about 0.000005368 second. What is this estimated time written as a single digit times a power of 10?

Name _____

Use the bank below to complete each sentence.

digit	estimate	exponent	greater than	less than
negative	positive	power of 10	rounded	small

1. $0.000527 = 5.27 \times 10^{-4}$

   a. The number 0.000527 is a very ☐ number.

   b. Since you move the decimal point 4 places to the right, the ☐ is negative.

   c. When the value of the original number is ☐ 1, the exponent is negative.

2. $61,253,221,000 \approx 6 \times 10^{10}$

   a. The number sentence above shows a(n) ☐.

   b. You can round 61,253,221,000 to the greatest place value and write it as a single digit times a(n) ☐.

   c. Since the original number is ☐ 1, the exponent is ☐.

3. The number 0.0000375 can be estimated by rounding to its greatest place value.

   a. The number 0.0000375 can be ☐ to 4×10^{-5} which is expressed in ☐.

   b. The rounded number is a single ☐ times a power of 10.

   c. The exponent is ☐ because the value of the number is less than 1.

Name _____

Read the problem below. Then answer the questions to help you understand the problem.

The average distance from Earth to the Sun is about 92,955,807 miles. In March 2029, Mars and the Sun will be in opposite directions from each other as seen from Earth, so Mars will be about 60,421,000 miles from Earth. The distance from Earth to the Sun will be about how many times greater than the distance from Mars to the Sun at this time?

1. Underline the question that you must answer.

2. Highlight the distances given in the problem. Then complete the diagram.

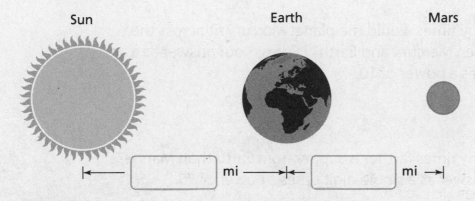

Sun   Earth   Mars

3. What operation will you use to solve the problem? Highlight the words that indicate the operation.

4. Do you need to find an exact answer or an estimate? Explain.

5. How can you use powers of 10 to help you solve the problem?

Name _____

The table shows the diameters of Mercury, Mars, and Jupiter, as well as their distances from Earth.

Planet	Diameter (km)	Distance from Earth (km)
Mercury	4,878	91,691,000
Mars	6,780	78,340,000
Jupiter	139,822	628,730,000

1. Use a single digit times a power of 10 to estimate Mercury's diameter and its distance from Earth.

2. About how many times would the planet Mercury fit across the distance between Mercury and Earth? Express your answer as a single digit times a power of 10.

3. About how many times farther is Jupiter from Earth than Mars is? Express your answer as a single digit times a power of 10.

4. Use a single digit times a power of 10 to estimate the diameter of Jupiter. About how many times greater is Jupiter's diameter than Mercury's? Express your answer as a single digit times a power of 10.

5. Neptune's diameter is about 5×10^4 km, and its distance from Earth is about 8×10^4 times its diameter. About how far is Neptune from Earth? Express the distance as a single digit times a power of 10 and show your work.

How do you write the number 0.0513 in scientific notation?

Step 1 Write the first factor.
Move the decimal point to the
right of the first nonzero digit.

$0.0513 \longrightarrow 5.13$

Step 2 Write the second factor.
Count the number of digits before
the decimal point.

$0.0513 \longrightarrow 10^{-2}$

0.05.13

0.0513 written in scientific notation is 5.13×10^{-2}.

As of July 1, 2014, the population of India was about 1,267,000,000.
How can you write this number in scientific notation?

1. Move the decimal point to the right of the first digit. What is the
   first factor?

2. Count the number of digits after the decimal point. How many
   places did you move the decimal point?

3. Did you move the decimal point to the right or to the left? What
   does this tell you about the power of 10 in the second factor?

4. What is the second factor written as a power of 10?

5. Write the population of India in scientific notation.

On the Back!

6. There are 3,153,600 seconds in a year. How can you write this
   number in scientific notation?

Copyright © SAVVAS Learning Company LLC. All Rights Reserved.

Name _____

Choose the term from the list that *best* represents the item in each box.

estimate	negative exponent	power of 10	positive exponent
scientific notation	standard form	very large number	very small number

1. $3{,}200{,}000 = 3.2 \times \mathbf{10^6}$

2. $465{,}879{,}665{,}000$

3. $4.06 \times 10^7 = \mathbf{40{,}600{,}000}$

4. $421{,}341{,}778 \approx 4.2 \times 10^8$

5. 10^{-5}

6. 3.05×10^{-7}

7. 0.0000623

8. 9.45×10^{12}

Name _____

Read the problem below. Then answer the questions to help you understand the problem.

The diameter of the smallest grain of pollen is 0.0006 centimeter. How would you express this diameter in scientific notation?

1. Underline the question that you need to answer.

2. Circle the number that you must write in scientific notation. Is this number a large number or a small number?

3. A number written in scientific notation is a product of two factors. One of the factors is a power of 10. Describe the other factor.

4. What is the first step in writing 0.0006 in scientific notation?

5. Will your answer contain a positive power of 10 or a negative power of 10? Explain.

The table shows some data about the Earth.

Facts About Earth	
Radius at Equator	6378.1 km
Mass	5.8726×10^{24} kg
Volume	1,083,210,000,000 km³

1. Express Earth's radius in scientific notation.

2. Express Earth's radius in centimeters. Write your answer in scientific notation. Show how you found this measurement using the properties of exponents. (1 km = 1,000 m; 1 m = 100 cm)

3. Express Earth's volume in scientific notation.

4. If you write the mass of Earth in standard notation, how many zeros will you write?

5. The density of an object is found by dividing its mass by its volume. Express Earth's density using scientific notation in kg/km³.

6. A museum has a model of Earth with radius 3 meters. About how many times greater is Earth's actual radius than the model's radius? Express your answer in scientific notation. Show your work.

Name _____

Express the product $72 \times (3.4 \times 10^5)$ in scientific notation.

$(7.2 \times 10^1) \times (3.4 \times 10^5)$	Write an expression in scientific notation.
$(7.2 \times 3.4) \times (10^1 \times 10^5)$	Use the Associative Property to regroup.
$24.48 \times (10^6)$	Multiply and use the Product of Powers Property.
2.448×10^7	Write the product in scientific notation.

Estadio Azteca, a stadium in Mexico City, has a capacity of 1.04×10^5 people. One day, spectators filled Estadio Azteca in 25 minutes. What was the average number of people who entered the stadium per minute? Express your answer in scientific notation.

1. What division expression represents the average number of people per minute?

2. How would you express the divisor in scientific notation?

3. Rewrite your division expression from Exercise 1 with the divisor expressed in scientific notation.

4. Use the Associative Property to regroup. Then simplify.

5. In scientific notation, what was the average number of people who entered Estadio Azteca per minute?

On the Back!

6. The maximum speed of China's CRH380A train is 4.873×10^2 kilometers per hour. What is the greatest number of kilometers the train could travel in 16 hours? Express your answer in scientific notation.

Name _____

Use the bank below to complete each problem.

decimal point	exponent	factor	power of 10
Product of Powers Property	Quotient of Powers Property	scientific notation	standard form

1. Use the example provided to answer parts a–c.

   $(3 \times 10^6) \div 480 = (3 \times 10^6) \div (4.8 \times 10^2)$
   $\qquad\qquad\qquad = (3 \div 4.8) \times (10^6 \div 10^2)$
   $\qquad\qquad\qquad = 0.625 \times 10^4$
   $\qquad\qquad\qquad = 6{,}250$

   a. The number 480 was changed to 4.8 times a _____.

   b. By moving the _____ 4 places to the right, the solution is expressed in _____.

   c. This problem was solved using the _____.

2. Use the example provided to answer parts a–c.

   $(8.2 \times 10^{13}) - (7.85 \times 10^{10}) = (8.2 \times 10^{13}) - (0.00785 \times 10^{13})$
   $\qquad\qquad\qquad\qquad\qquad = (8.2 - 0.00785) \times 10^{13}$
   $\qquad\qquad\qquad\qquad\qquad = 8.19215 \times 10^{13}$

   a. The number 7.85×10^{10} was rewritten as 0.00785×10^{13} so that the _____ matches that of the first number.

   b. The solution is expressed in _____. The first _____ is a number greater than or equal to 1 and less than 10, and the second is a _____.

   c. This problem was solved using the _____.

Name _____

Build Mathematical Literacy
2-10

Read the problem below. Then answer the questions to help you understand the problem.

A grass soccer field has an area of 7.14×10^3 square meters. The Parks Department estimates that it will cost \$0.04 per square meter to reseed the field. About how much is the total cost of reseeding the field?

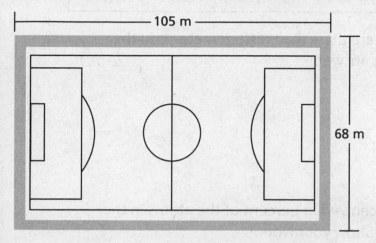

────── 105 m ──────

68 m

1. Underline the important information given in the problem.

2. What units will the answer have?

3. Explain why one of the given numbers will have to be rewritten in a different form.

4. What operation will you use to solve the problem? Which property can you use to help you perform the operation?

5. Does it make sense to give the answer to the problem in scientific notation? Explain.

M 2-10

Name _____

The average human body contains a total of 7×10^{27} atoms. The table below shows how many of those are hydrogen, nitrogen, radium, and gold atoms.

Type of Atom	Hydrogen	Nitrogen	Radium	Gold
Number of Atoms	4.22×10^{27}	3.9×10^{25}	8×10^{10}	2×10^{19}

1. How many more hydrogen atoms are there than nitrogen atoms in the average human body? Justify your answer.

2. To the nearest hundredth of a percent, what percent of the atoms in the human body are nitrogen atoms? Show your work.

3. There are about 100 times more gold atoms in the average human body than uranium atoms. About how many uranium atoms are there in the average human body?

4. There are about 2×10^{13} more chlorine atoms in the average human body than radium atoms. About how many chlorine atoms are there in the average human body? Show your work.

5. Estimate the ratio of hydrogen atoms to radium atoms. Express your answer in scientific notation and in standard form.

6. Explain why scientific notation is helpful when computing with large numbers.

Name _____

Analyze and Use Proportional Relationships

Dear Family,

   Your child is learning to solve problems involving proportional relationships. He or she is learning how to identify and use unit rates, determine whether relationships are proportional, and use proportional thinking.
   Here is an activity you can do with your child to help him or her develop fluency with proportional relationships.

Finding the Unit Rate

Materials: number cube

Step 1 Roll a number cube three times. Write 1 two-digit number and 1 one-digit number using the digits you rolled.

Step 2 Write a ratio using the two numbers, such as $\frac{26}{4}$.

Step 3 Find the corresponding unit rate, and suggest a situation where that unit rate might be found. For example, 4 movie tickets cost $26, so the unit rate is $6.50 per ticket. Your child may need to round the unit rate.

Step 4 Write an equation for the proportional relationship you found.

Observe Your Child

Focus on Mathematical Practices
Make sense of problems and persevere in solving them.

Help your child become proficient with this Mathematical Practice. Have your child explain what the initial ratio means and describe how the unit rate expresses the same idea in a different way.

Nombre _____

Analizar y usar relaciones proporcionales

Estimada familia:

   Su hijo o hija está aprendiendo a resolver problemas sobre relaciones de proporción. Está aprendiendo a identificar y a usar tasas por unidad, a determinar si las relaciones son de proporción y a usar el razonamiento proporcional.

   Esta es una actividad que puede realizar con su hijo o hija para ayudarlo(a) a adquirir fluidez con las relaciones de proporción.

Hallar la tasa por unidad

Materiales: Cubo numérico

Paso 1 Lancen un cubo numérico tres veces. Con los números que obtuvieron, escriban un número de dos dígitos y un número de un dígito.

Paso 2 Escriban una razón que incluya ambos números, como $\frac{26}{4}$.

Paso 3 Hallen la tasa por unidad correspondiente y sugieran una situación en que se podría hallar esa tasa por unidad. Por ejemplo, 4 boletos de cine cuestan $26; por tanto, la tasa por unidad es $6.50 por boleto. Es posible que sea necesario redondear la tasa por unidad.

Paso 4 Escriban una ecuación para la relación de proporción que hallaron.

Observe a su hijo o hija

Enfoque en las Prácticas matemáticas
Entender problemas y perseverar en resolverlos.

Ayude a su hijo o hija a adquirir competencia en esta Práctica matemática. Pídale que explique qué significa la razón inicial y que describa de qué manera la tasa por unidad expresa la misma idea de otro modo.

Mammalian Marathon

There are over 7 million animal species in the world. Each species has an average running pace. The fastest mammal on Earth is the cheetah, which can run as fast as 69.5 miles per hour (mi/h). The slowest mammal on earth is the three-toed sloth, which creeps along at about 0.08 mi/h.

Humans race against each other and a wide variety of animals. Sometimes humans ride on animals, such as horses or camels, as they race toward a finish line. Other races involve a single type of animal (greyhounds, hamsters, or mice, for example) racing against each other.

Your Project **Predict Race Results**

What are some fast animals you can think of? What are some slow ones? How fast can you run? Think about how you could predict who would win a race.

Research the speed of at least four different animals. Then time how long it takes you to run $\frac{1}{4}$ mile (1 lap around a track). If you and these four types of animals ran a marathon (26.2 miles) at those speeds, who would win? How far into the race would the four other racers be when the winner crossed the finish line? Write a sports article or record a sports newscast to predict the outcome of this race. Use the information you learned in this topic to justify your predictions.

Name _____

The Olympic Games

Every two years, countries come together to compete in a series of sporting events known as the Olympic Games. The Games alternate between Summer and Winter. The Summer Olympic Games involve sports such as baseball, soccer, diving, and judo. The Winter Olympic Games involve sports practiced on snow and ice, such as skiing, curling, and figure skating. The first modern Olympics took place in 1896 in Athens, but its origins date back to ancient Greece.

Your Project **Calculate the Weight of Your Pack**

Suppose it is the year 5054. Humans now travel the universe. The popularity of the Olympics has spread beyond Earth, becoming an intergalactic event with sporting events spread across several planets. One of the challenges (and advantages) of having events spread across several planets is that the gravity on each planet is different.

You are preparing to compete in your first Intergalactic Olympics, during which you will travel to at least three planets (from the table below). All athletes must complete a registration packet that includes a travel summary page for the planning of shuttle flights. The travel summary requires the following information: your sport, the contents of your training bag, and how much the bag will weigh on each planet you are visiting. It also asks if you will need assistance with your training bag on any planet.

Your training bag includes at least five items. Provide the information necessary to complete the travel summary for your registration packet.

PLANET	GRAVITY RELATIVE TO EARTH
A	0.738
B	0.971
C	0.598
D	1.13
E	0.061
F	0.156
G	2.14
H	0.438

Name _____

What's *Your* Story?

Many math problems are short stories. They start with a situation or event and invite the reader to wonder about the ending. A short story may have as few as five words or as many as five thousand words. It may have several characters or only one. It may include illustrations or leave the images up to the reader's imagination. A good short story appeals to the reader's emotions and grabs the reader's attention in the first sentence.

Your Project **Write a Short Story**

Write and illustrate a short story that includes at least three proportional relationships. Use a scenario from this topic or one of your own. Explain why proportional relationships are important to the story and how they help or impact the main character.

Name _____

Sounds of Music

The size of an instrument determines the range of pitches it can produce. A guitar produces lower pitches than a violin, and a cello produces lower pitches than a guitar.

There are other ways to control the sound an instrument produces, however. *Where* you press a guitar string affects the pitch of the string when you pluck it—pressing halfway along the string produces a pitch an octave higher than pressing the top of the string. How a piano is tuned affects the pitch of a string when you play a note.

Your Project **Play Music**

Think about any musical instruments that have a symbolic or cultural importance to you and your family. Research how composers and musicians use ratios and proportions in music. Find or compose a piece of music and identify three ratios between notes. Make a video of yourself playing the piece of music. In your video, include a segment in which you explain how the changes in pitch are proportionally related.

Name _____

An Essential Resource

Water Availability

Most of Earth is covered by water. Only a small portion of that water is fresh water that is useable for human survival. Complete this page to explore the quantity and distribution of fresh water on Earth. If you struggle with your research, try the following questions to get you started.

- Where is Earth's water?
- How much water is on Earth?
- What is the distribution of water on Earth?

Part A   Research different types of water sources and complete the table.

Salt Water	Fresh Water
Sources List the different types of sources of each type of water.	
Percent of all water on Earth	

Part B   Which fresh water sources are easily accessible surface water?

Part C   What are some fresh water sources in your state? Are they big enough to supply all your state's water needs?

An Essential Resource

Water Needs

Each person should drink 64 ounces of water a day.
Additionally, tasks around the house also use water.
How much water does a household use?
If you struggle with your research, try the following phrases to get you started.

- US water use
- American daily water use

Part A   Create a table showing all the tasks you and your family do around the house that use water and how often those tasks happen. Leave space for one more column.

Part B   Research the amount of water each task uses and record that amount in a new column in your table above.

Part C   Using your information from Parts A and B, estimate your family's water use for one week. Show your work.

An Essential Resource

Water Needs, *continued*

Part D Using proportional relationships, estimate how much water your family will use over the following lengths of time. Show your work.

1 month: _____   6 months: _____   12 months: _____

Part E Create a graph showing your family's estimated water use over time.

Part F Describe at least 3 ways your family can reduce the amount of water you use.

Name _____

An Essential Resource

Water Access and Collection

**What are other ways to get water if you do not have access to municipal water?
Research various alternative water sources and collection methods.
Complete the table using the information from your research.
If you struggle with your research, try the following phrases to get you started.**

- Methods used to collect water
- Water source implementation tools
- Alternative water sources

Water Source	How to Access the Water	Quality Concerns	Appropriate Water Uses

Name _____

An Essential Resource

Product Design

Your task: Design an alternative water supply system for a village without a municipal water supply.

Describe existing products and how you wish to improve on them.

What requirements do you need to meet to successfully complete your task? If needs are conflicting, which take priority?

How will you determine your success in completing your task?

Brainstorm and describe three products that could fit your needs.

An Essential Resource

Product Design, *continued*

On a scale from 1–3, rank how well each product meets your requirements.

Criteria	Product #1: _____	Product #2: _____	Product #3: _____
Requirement #1: _____			
Requirement #2: _____			
Requirement #3: _____			
Requirement #4: _____			
Requirement #5: _____			
Total Points			
Notes			

Which product is the best choice to complete your task? Why?

A ratio is a relationship in which for every x units of one quantity there are y units of another quantity. There are three ways to write the ratio that relates the number of squares to the number of triangles.

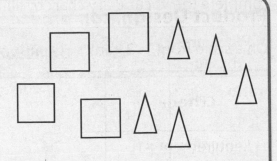

$\frac{4}{5}$ 4 : 5   4 to 5

You can find equivalent ratios by multiplying or dividing both terms of a given ratio by the same nonzero number.

$\overset{\times 3}{\frac{8}{10}} = \overset{}{\underset{\times 3}{\frac{24}{30}}}$ $\overset{\div 2}{\frac{8}{10}} = \underset{\div 2}{\frac{4}{5}}$

Alyssa's lemonade recipe calls for 9 lemons for every 2.5 gallons of water. Brian's recipe calls for 12 lemons for every 4 gallons of water. Whose lemonade will require more water if they each use 36 lemons?

1. Complete the tables of equivalent ratios to find out how much water each recipe requires if 36 lemons are used.

Alyssa	
Number of Lemons	Gallons of Water
9	2.5
18	5
	7.5
	10

× ☐   × 3

Brian	
Number of Lemons	Gallons of Water
12	4
24	

2. How many gallons of water will Alyssa need?

3. How many gallons of water will Brian need?

4. Whose recipe requires more water?

On the Back!

5. Mayumi hikes 3 miles in 2 hours. Edwin hikes 4 miles in 3 hours. Who takes more time to complete a 12-mile hiking trail? How much more time?

Name _____

Complete the vocabulary chart by filling in the missing information.

Word or Phrase	Definition	Picture or Example
ratio		4 to 3, 4 : 3, or $\frac{4}{3}$
equivalent ratios	Equivalent ratios are ratios that have different numbers but represent the same relationship. They can be found by multiplying or dividing both terms of a given ratio by the same nonzero number.	
rate		$\frac{250 \text{ miles}}{5 \text{ hours}}$ $\frac{36 \text{ eggs}}{3 \text{ cartons}}$
unit rate	A unit rate compares x units of one quantity to 1 unit of another quantity.	
unit price		$0.45 per apple

**Read the word problem below. Then answer the questions
to identify the steps for solving the problem.**

Miguel pays $42.99 per month at Be Fit Gym. Jina pays $215.94 every 6 months at
Main Street Gym. Which gym is more expensive? How much more does membership at
that gym cost each month?

1. Underline the two questions that you need to answer.

2. Circle the information you are given in the problem.

3. Can you compare the two dollar amounts exactly as they are
    given in the problem? Explain.

4. What is the first step in solving the problem?

5. One student finds the number of months for $1 and another finds
    the number of dollars for 1 month. Which unit rate is more helpful
    in solving the problem?

6. What two pieces of information must you include in order to give
    a complete solution for this problem?

Name _____

Kyle plays softball. His goal is to have a batting average of .400 or greater by the end of the season. The ratio that relates the number of hits to the number of chances, called at-bats, is used to determine batting average in baseball and softball.

$$\text{batting average} = \frac{\text{number of hits}}{\text{number of at-bats}}$$

So far this season, Kyle has 25 hits. He has been at bat 65 times. He expects to have 10 more at-bats this season.

1. What is Kyle's current batting average?

2. Let h represent the number of hits that Kyle gets in his last 10 at-bats of the season. Write a ratio that represents Kyle's batting average at the end of the season.

3. What values of h make sense for the ratio you wrote? Explain.

4. Is it possible for Kyle to reach or exceed his goal? Use ratios to justify your answer.

5. What is the least number of additional at-bats that Kyle needs in order to reach his goal? Explain.

Name _____

A train moves at a constant speed. The train travels 13 miles in $\frac{1}{6}$ hour.
What is the train's speed in miles per hour?

Step 1 Make a table of equivalent ratios.

×2 ×3 ×4 ×5 ×6

Miles	13	26	39	52	65	78
Hours	$\frac{1}{6}$	$\frac{2}{6}$	$\frac{3}{6}$	$\frac{4}{6}$	$\frac{5}{6}$	$\frac{6}{6}=1$

Step 2 Identify the unit rate. The train travels $\frac{78\text{ miles}}{1\text{ hour}}$, or 78 miles per hour.

An elevator in a skyscraper rises 240 feet in $\frac{1}{5}$ minute. What is the
elevator's rate in feet per minute?

1. Complete the table of equivalent ratios.

×2 ×3 ×4 ×5

Feet	240				
Minutes	$\frac{1}{5}$	$\frac{2}{5}$	$\frac{3}{5}$	$\frac{4}{5}$	$\frac{5}{5}=1$

2. Use the ratio $\frac{240}{\frac{1}{5}}$. What operation can you do on both terms to find
   an equivalent ratio that has 1 as the second term?

3. What is the elevator's rate in feet per minute?

On the Back!

4. Elijah drives 9 miles to his friend's house in $\frac{1}{6}$ hour. How fast does
   Elijah drive, in miles per hour? If he drives at this rate for 2 hours,
   how far does he drive?

Each section of the graphic organizer contains a vocabulary term and two examples. Use each item from the list below to complete the graphic organizer.

complex fraction	16 oranges for $4	$\dfrac{4.5 \text{ cups of juice}}{1 \text{ pitcher}}$
unit rate	$\dfrac{\frac{1}{2}}{\frac{2}{3}}$	17 feet per second

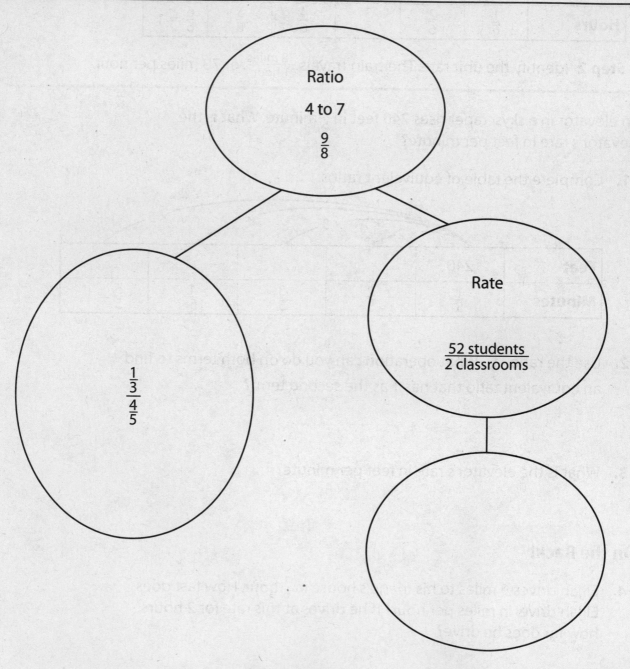

Ratio

4 to 7

$\dfrac{9}{8}$

$\dfrac{\frac{1}{3}}{\frac{4}{5}}$

Rate

$\dfrac{52 \text{ students}}{2 \text{ classrooms}}$

Name _____

Review the Key Concept from the lesson. Then answer the questions to help you understand how to read a Key Concept.

🔍 **KEY CONCEPT**

You can use what you know about equivalent ratios and operations with fractions to write a ratio of fractions as a unit rate.

Tia skateboards $\frac{2}{3}$ mile for every $\frac{1}{6}$ hour.

$$\frac{\frac{2}{3}}{\frac{1}{6}} = \frac{\frac{2}{3} \times \frac{6}{1}}{\frac{1}{6} \times \frac{6}{1}} = \frac{4}{1} = 4$$

		$\times \frac{6}{1}$	
Miles	$\frac{2}{3}$	4
Hours	$\frac{1}{6}$	1
		$\times \frac{6}{1}$	

She skateboards 4 miles per hour.

---

1. Circle the first ratio of fractions in the Key Concept box.

2. How does the complex fraction show you how to write the ratio of fractions as a unit rate?

3. How are the calculations shown in the table like the calculations with the complex fraction?

4. Does it matter whether you use a complex fraction or a table to find a unit rate? Explain.

Jamar and his family frequently drive from their home in Riverside, California, to Jamar's grandparents' house in Tucson, Arizona. Because much of the drive is across the desert, Jamar's parents are usually able to drive at a constant rate for the entire trip. Some data about a typical one-way trip are shown below.

Data for a Typical One-Way Trip

- The car's gas tank holds 11 gallons of gas.
- It takes $\frac{1}{4}$ tank of gas to make $\frac{1}{6}$ of the trip.
- The car uses $\frac{2}{5}$ gallon of gas to travel $11\frac{1}{5}$ miles.
- The car travels $5\frac{1}{2}$ miles in 6 minutes.

---

1. Write a unit rate that describes the number of tanks of gas required per trip.

2. Write a unit rate that describes how far the car travels per gallon of gas.

3. Explain how you can determine the total distance of the one-way trip.

4. At what rate, in miles per hour, do Jamar's parents drive?

5. Write a unit rate that describes how long the one-way trip takes in hours and minutes per trip.

Two quantities have a proportional relationship if all of the ratios that relate the quantities are equivalent. This table shows a proportional relationship because all of the ratios $\frac{y}{x}$ are equivalent to 4.

x	2	4	5	6	7	10
y	8	16	20	24	28	40
$\frac{y}{x}$	$\frac{8}{2}=4$	$\frac{16}{4}=4$	$\frac{20}{5}=4$	$\frac{24}{6}=4$	$\frac{28}{7}=4$	$\frac{40}{10}=4$

Sophie records the total number of cans of cat food she uses after different numbers of days. She wants to know if the number of cans of cat food she uses is proportional to the number of days.

| After 3 days – 6 cans |
| After 4 days – 8 cans |
| After 9 days – 18 cans |

1. Complete the table.

Number of Days (x)	3	4	9
Number of Cans (y)	6	8	18
$\dfrac{\text{Number of Cans (y)}}{\text{Number of Days (x)}}$	$\frac{6}{3}=2$	$\frac{\square}{\square}=\square$	$\frac{\square}{\square}=\square$

2. Is the number of cans of cat food used proportional to the number of days? Explain.

3. How many cans of cat food will Sophie use after 12 days?

On the Back!

4. Is the relationship between the number of books and the number of shelves proportional? Explain.

Number of Shelves (x)	Number of Books (y)
3	135
5	225
6	270

Name _____

Use each of these words once to complete the sentences.

| equivalent | equivalent ratios | proportional | proportional relationship |

1. The fraction $\frac{1}{4}$ is _____ to the decimal 0.25.

2. Each egg carton holds 12 eggs. The number of eggs is
   _____ to the number of egg cartons.

3. Because $\frac{45 \text{ dogs}}{15 \text{ cats}}$ and $\frac{15 \text{ dogs}}{5 \text{ cats}}$ are both equivalent to $\frac{3 \text{ dogs}}{1 \text{ cat}}$,
   the number of dogs and the number of cats are in a
   _____.

4. The ratios $\frac{4}{16}$ and $\frac{1}{4}$ are examples of _____.

In each table, shade the row that contains the information you can use to determine whether the relationship between the quantities is proportional. Then circle *proportional* or *not proportional*.

5.

Time in Hours (x)	3	4
Distance in Miles (y)	180	240
$\dfrac{\text{Distance in Miles } (y)}{\text{Time in Hours } (x)}$	60	60

Proportional   Not proportional

6.

Number of Tanks (x)	1	3
Number of Fish (y)	12	39
$\dfrac{\text{Number of Fish } (y)}{\text{Number of Tanks } (x)}$	12	13

Proportional   Not proportional

Name _____

Read the problem below. Then answer the questions to understand the problem.

The table below gives the prices of rose corsages at John's Flower Shop.
Is there a proportional relationship between the number of roses in a corsage and the price of the corsage?

Number of Roses	Price ($)
1	5
2	10
3	15
4	20

1. Underline the question that you need to answer.

2. What is a proportional relationship between two quantities?

3. What information is given in the table?

4. What do you need to do to answer the question?

5. What ratios can you use to determine whether the relationship is proportional?

Name _____

Is there a proportional relationship between the area of an enlarged rectangle and the area of the original rectangle? Use the rectangles below to explore this question.

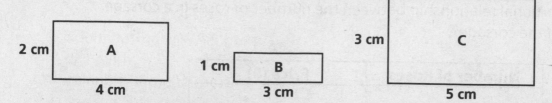

2 cm | A | 4 cm

1 cm | B | 3 cm

3 cm | C | 5 cm

1. Find the area of each rectangle. Then find the area of each rectangle when all of its dimensions are multiplied by 2. Record your results in the table.

2. Are the area of the enlarged rectangle and the area of the original rectangle in a proportional relationship?

Rectangle	Area of Original Rectangle (cm²)	Area of Enlarged Rectangle (cm²)
A		
B		
C		

3. Suppose you multiply all of the original dimensions by 5. Is the relationship between the area of the enlarged rectangle and the area of the original rectangle a proportional relationship? Explain.

4. Suppose you multiply all of the original dimensions of a rectangle by n. What will the ratio $\dfrac{\text{Area of enlarged rectangle (cm}^2)}{\text{Area of original rectangle (cm}^2)}$ be?

5. A student wants to multiply all of the dimensions of Rectangle A by 7. Explain how the student can find the area of the enlarged rectangle without calculating its dimensions.

Name _____

Jack uses 1.5 cups of water for every 2 cups of raspberries to make a raspberry syrup. What is an equation that relates the amount of water to the amount of raspberries in the syrup?

Step 1 Are the quantities proportional?

Cups of Raspberries (x)	2	4	6
Cups of Water (y)	1.5	3	4.5
$\frac{y}{x}$	$\frac{1.5}{2} = 0.75$	$\frac{3}{4} = 0.75$	$\frac{4.5}{6} = 0.75$

The quantities are proportional. The constant of proportionality is 0.75.

Step 2 Write an equation in the form $y = kx$, where k is the constant of proportionality, to relate proportional quantities x and y.

Use $k = 0.75$. $y = kx$

$y = 0.75x$

The equation $y = 0.75x$ relates the amount of water to the amount of raspberries.

1. Complete the table to determine whether the quantities x and y are proportional.

x	2	5	7
y	4.5	11.25	15.75
$\frac{y}{x}$	$\frac{4.5}{2} = \boxed{}$	$\frac{11.25}{\boxed{}} = \boxed{}$	$\frac{\boxed{}}{7} = \boxed{}$

2. What is the constant of proportionality that relates the quantities x and y?

$\frac{y}{x} = \boxed{}$

3. Write an equation that relates the quantities.

$y = kx$

$y = \boxed{}\,x$

On the Back!

4. The table shows how the quantities x and y are related. Are the quantities proportional? Write an equation to represent the relationship.

x	5	7	9
y	6.5	9.1	11.7

Use the terms from the list below to complete the sentences.
Each term will be used once.

constant of proportionality	ratio	equivalent ratios
proportional relationship	table	equation

It takes a machine 10 seconds to fill 4 bottles of juice. It takes 15 seconds
to fill 6 bottles of juice. Does this describe a proportional relationship?

1. Make a(n) _____ to organize the data.

Time (t)	Number of Bottles (b)
10	4
15	6

2. Find each _____ that
   compares the number of bottles
   to the time in seconds. These are

   _____ .

Time (t)	Number of Bottles (b)	$\dfrac{\text{Number of Bottles } (b)}{\text{Time } (t)}$
10	4	$\dfrac{4}{10} = 0.4$
15	6	$\dfrac{6}{15} = 0.4$

3. There is a(n) _____ between
   the number of bottles and the time.

4. The _____ is 0.4.

5. A(n) _____ that represents the relationship can
   be written as $b = 0.4t$, where t represents the number of seconds
   and b represents the number of bottles.

Name _____

**Read the problem. Then answer the questions to
help you write an equation.**

The Drama Club members sell magazine subscriptions to raise money.
The total amount raised increases by $5 for every 10 subscriptions sold.
Write an equation to represent this situation.

1. Circle the words that describe the quantities involved in the
   problem.

2. Underline the sentence in the
   problem that describes how
   the quantities are related.
   Then complete the table.
   Include a title for the quantity
   in the first column.

	Total Amount Raised ($)
10	5
20	
30	

3. How does the table help you see the relationship between the
   two quantities?

4. Circle the equation below that represents the relationship in the
   problem. Tell what x and y represent and explain your choice.

   $y = 0.5x$ $y = 5x$ $y = 10x$

Name _____

You may have heard the phrase *at a snail's pace* used to refer to something moving very slowly. How fast does a snail travel? A 2013 study conducted in Exeter, England, measured the speed of garden snails. The table shows how far a snail can travel when it is moving at its top speed.

1. Write an equation that relates the number of inches, d, that a snail can move at its top speed to the number of minutes, m, that the snail is moving.

Time (min)	Distance (in.)
3	2
6	4
9	6

2. Use your equation to write a new equation that represents the distance in inches, d, that a snail can move in h hours, assuming it always moves at its top speed. Explain.

3. Write an equation that represents the distance in feet, f, that a snail can move in h hours, assuming it always moves at its top speed. Explain.

4. What is the constant of proportionality in the last equation you wrote? What does it represent?

5. If a snail could move at top speed for a full day without resting, how far would it travel?

Name _____

The graph of a proportional relationship is a straight line through the origin, (0, 0).

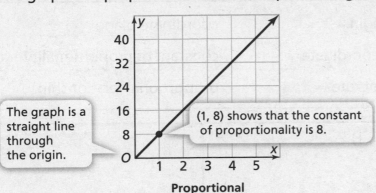

The graph is a straight line through the origin.

(1, 8) shows that the constant of proportionality is 8.

Proportional

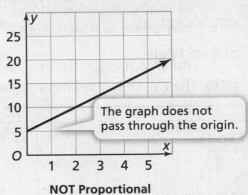

The graph does not pass through the origin.

NOT Proportional

Mark is planning a birthday party at the local skating rink. The table shows the rates that are charged for parties at the skating rink. Is the number of guests proportional to the cost? If so, what is the constant of proportionality, and what does it mean in this situation?

Number of Guests (x)	Cost ($) (y)
5	60
10	120
15	180
20	240

1. Graph the ordered pairs on a coordinate plane.

2. Is the graph a straight line?

   YES or **NO**

3. Does the graph go through the origin, (0, 0)?

   YES or **NO**

4. Is the cost proportional to the number of guests?

   YES or **NO**

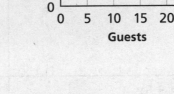

5. What is the constant of proportionality, $\frac{y}{x}$?

   $\frac{y}{x} = \frac{\Box}{\Box} = \Box$

6. The constant of proportionality describes how the quantities are related. The cost of each guest at the party is $\Box$.

On the Back!

7. Draw an example of a graph of a proportional relationship. Identify the constant of proportionality.

Choose the term from the list that best represents the item in each box.

equivalent ratios	origin	coordinate plane
ordered pair	x-coordinate	constant of proportionality
ratio	unit rate	proportional relationship

1.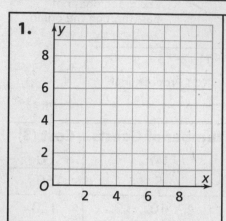

2. (5, 1)

3. $\frac{5}{6}$

4. 40 miles per hour

5. $\frac{7}{15}$ and $\frac{21}{45}$

6.

7. $y = 3.5x$

8.

9. (7, 12)

Name _____

Read the problem and connect it to the graph.

A company ships bottles of olive oil to stores in boxes. The graph shows a proportional relationship between the number of boxes shipped and the number of bottles of olive oil shipped. About how many bottles are shipped in 8 boxes?

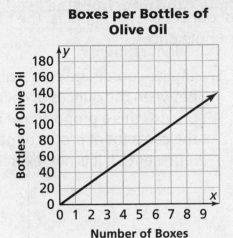

Boxes per Bottles of Olive Oil

1. Underline the name of the quantity that is on the horizontal axis of the graph. Circle the name of the quantity that is on the vertical axis.

2. How can you tell that the graph represents a proportional relationship?

3. Find the point (0, 0) on the graph. How can you find what the x- and y-coordinates of this point represent?

4. What does the point (0, 0) mean?

5. How can you use the graph to determine how many bottles are shipped in 8 boxes? Draw lines on the graph to help find the answer.

Name _____

Katie starts a business selling organic dried chili peppers online. She decides that customers can order any number of ounces of chili peppers. The table shows some sample prices.

Online Chili Pepper Sales

Chili Peppers (ounces)	Price ($)
3	$7.50
5	$12.50
6	$15.00

1. On the coordinate plane, graph the relationship between the ounces of chili peppers and their price. Is this a proportional relationship? If it is, find the constant of proportionality, and tell what it represents. If it is not, explain why not.

2. Katie decides to increase the price of the chili peppers by $1 per ounce. Draw a graph of the new relationship on the same coordinate plane.

3. How does the second graph compare to the first graph? Is the relationship still proportional? Explain.

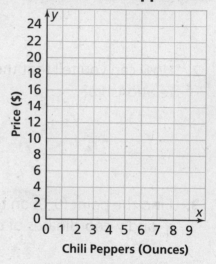

Online Chili Pepper Sales

4. After increasing the prices by $1 per ounce, Katie realizes that she needs to charge customers for shipping. She decides to charge $5 for shipping no matter how many ounces of chili peppers are purchased. Draw a graph of this new relationship on the same coordinate plane.

5. How does the third graph compare to the second graph? Is the relationship still proportional? Explain.

6. Write an equation that can be used to determine the total cost of the chili peppers and the shipping in dollars, y, when a customer orders x ounces of chili peppers.

Name _____

It is important to determine how quantities in a problem situation
are related to determine whether you can use proportional reasoning.

**Gabrielle is 15 and Alex is 12. Do their
ages form a proportional relationship?**

Graph a coordinate pair for their present
ages on a coordinate plane and graph a
coordinate pair for their ages in 6 years.

Draw a line through their ages and
extend the line. The relationship is not
proportional because the line does not
pass through the origin.

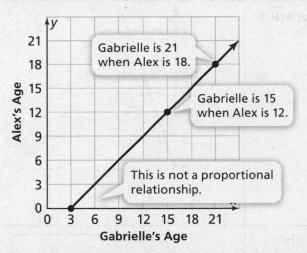

Gabrielle is 21 when Alex is 18.

Gabrielle is 15 when Alex is 12.

This is not a proportional relationship.

Alex's Age

Gabrielle's Age

**Sally collected 32 coins. The ratio of Sally's coins to Bill's coins is 4 : 7.
If Sally and Bill each double the number of coins they have now,
what is the ratio of Sally's coins to Bill's coins?**

1. Use equivalent ratios to find the number of coins
    Bill has. Let b = the number of Bill's coins.

    $$\frac{4}{\boxed{}} = \frac{32}{b}$$

    Bill has $\boxed{}$ coins.

    $$\frac{4 \times 8}{\boxed{} \times \boxed{}} = \frac{32}{\boxed{}}$$

2. Find the ratio after they each double their number of coins.

    Sally will have 2 × 32 = $\boxed{}$ coins. Bill will have 2 × $\boxed{}$ = $\boxed{}$ coins.

    The ratio of the number of Sally's coins to the number of Bill's coins is now $\dfrac{\boxed{}}{\boxed{}}$.

3. How does this new ratio compare to the original ratio 4 : 7?

On the Back!

4. A gift shop sells fruit baskets that each contain 4 apples and 3 oranges. If
    the shop owner orders 24 apples and 20 oranges, some fruit will be left over.
    How should the owner adjust the order so there is no fruit left over? Explain.

Name ________________________________

Additional Vocabulary Support
3-6

Determine whether each situation in the graphic organizer represents a proportional relationship. Write *proportional* or *not proportional*.

<table>
<tr><td>Graphs</td><td>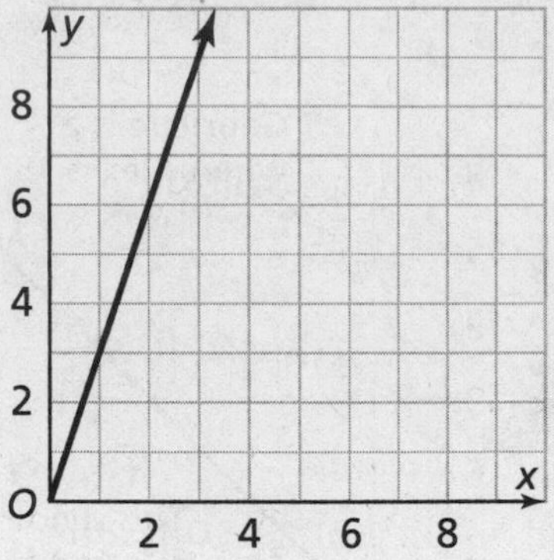</td><td>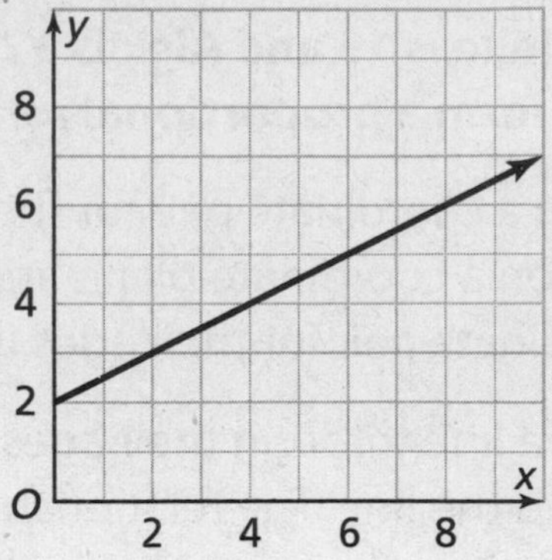</td></tr>
<tr><td>Tables</td><td><table><tr><th>x</th><th>y</th></tr><tr><td>4</td><td>6</td></tr><tr><td>8</td><td>12</td></tr><tr><td>12</td><td>24</td></tr><tr><td>16</td><td>30</td></tr></table></td><td><table><tr><th>x</th><th>y</th></tr><tr><td>2.5</td><td>5</td></tr><tr><td>5</td><td>10</td></tr><tr><td>7.5</td><td>15</td></tr><tr><td>15</td><td>30</td></tr></table></td></tr>
<tr><td>Ratios</td><td>$\frac{1}{3}$ $\frac{2}{5}$ $\frac{3}{8}$</td><td>$\frac{20}{30}$ $\frac{40}{60}$ $\frac{60}{90}$</td></tr>
<tr><td>Words</td><td>Diego drives 110 miles in 2 hours, 165 miles in 3 hours, and 220 miles in 4 hours.</td><td>Amy is 2 years older than Colin.</td></tr>
</table>

Name _____

Read the problem below. Answer the questions to help you understand the problem.

In Janelle's playlist, the ratio of pop songs to country songs is 6 : 5. There are 20 country songs. How many pop songs will she have if she doubles the number of each type of music on her playlist?

1. Choose the statement that will help you solve this problem. Explain your choice.

   ☐ The graph of a proportional relationship is a straight line through the origin.

   ☐ When two quantities are in a proportional relationship, all of the ratios that relate the quantities are equivalent.

   ☐ You can write a ratio involving fractions as a complex fraction.

2. If you multiply both terms of a ratio by the same nonzero number, does the ratio change? Explain your answer.

3. Use the information in the problem and proportional reasoning to complete the table. What other step is needed to solve the problem?

Comparison	Equivalent Ratios
Pop songs _____ ⬚	× ⬚ ⬚ → ⬚ 5 → 20 × 4

Name _____

In 2005, scientists determined the ideal mixture of sand and water for building a sand castle. The graph shows the relationship between the number of cups of sand and the number of cups of water to create the ideal mixture.

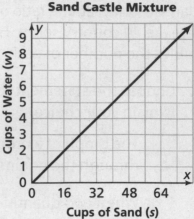

Sand Castle Mixture

Cups of Water (w) — y-axis labeled 0 through 9

Cups of Sand (s) — x-axis labeled 0, 16, 32, 48, 64

1. Write an equation that you can use to find the ideal number of cups of water, *w*, that you should add when you have a container with *s* cups of sand.

2. Marcus and Chloe are building a sand castle using the ideal mixture of sand and water. They have partly filled a container with the ideal mixture. Marcus adds 3 cups of sand to the container. How much water should Chloe add to keep the ideal ratio of water to sand? Explain.

3. Starting with an ideal mixture of sand and water, Marcus adds 2 cups of water to the mixture. How much sand should Chloe add to keep the ideal ratio of water to sand?

4. Marcus and Chloe determine that they will need 108 cups of the ideal mixture of sand and water in order to build a new sand castle. How much sand and water should they use to make the mixture? Justify your answer.

Analyze and Solve Percent Problems

Dear Family,

Your child is learning to solve problems involving percents. He or she is learning to apply proportions and the percent equation to a variety of contexts, including percent change, percent markup and markdown, percent error, and simple interest.

Here is an activity to help your child practice using percents.

Find the Best Markdown

Materials: Store advertisements from newspaper inserts or sale signs in stores

As you are shopping or looking through advertisements with your child, look for signs that give an original price and a sale price. Ask your child to calculate the percent markdown. Record the original price, sale price, and percent markdown for several items. Then determine which item had the greatest percent markdown.

Observe Your Child

Focus on Mathematical Practices
Reason abstractly and quantitatively.

Help your child become proficient with this Mathematical Practice. Ask him or her whether the greatest percent markdown is also the markdown of the greatest amount. Discuss why a markdown given as a percent does not tell the amount of the markdown in dollars.

Analizar y resolver problemas de porcentaje

> Estimada familia:
>
> Su hijo o hija está aprendiendo a resolver problemas sobre porcentajes. Está aprendiendo a aplicar proporciones y la ecuación de porcentaje a diversos contextos, como cambios porcentuales, márgenes de ganancia y rebajas porcentuales, errores porcentuales e interés simple.
>
> Esta es una actividad que puede ayudar a su hijo o hija a practicar el uso de porcentajes.

Hallar la rebaja más conveniente

Materiales: Anuncios publicitarios de tiendas, tomados de periódicos o de carteles de ofertas de tiendas

Cuando vaya de compras o analice anuncios publicitarios con su hijo o hija, busquen aquellos que brindan el precio original y el precio rebajado. Pídale que calcule la rebaja porcentual. Anoten el precio original, el precio rebajado y la rebaja porcentual de distintos artículos. Luego, determinen qué artículo tiene la rebaja porcentual más conveniente.

Observe a su hijo o hija

Enfoque en las Prácticas matemáticas
Razonar de manera abstracta y cuantitativa.

Ayude a su hijo o hija a adquirir competencia en esta Práctica matemática. Pregúntele si la mayor rebaja porcentual corresponde también a la rebaja del monto mayor. Comenten por qué una rebaja que se expresa como un porcentaje no indica la cantidad de dinero de la rebaja en dólares.

Name _____

Retail Appeal

Advertisements, sales, and coupons are just some of the ways store owners encourage people to come inside and start shopping. A store has to sell a certain amount of merchandise each month just to break even—the point at which expenses and income are equal—and it has to sell more than that to make a profit. A store's expenses include its inventory, or the items on its shelves; salaries for the employees; and rent for the space.

Your Project **Search for Bargains**

Select at least three items that you want to purchase from one or more stores. One should be something on sale or available at a discount. One should be something from the sporting goods section. One should be a toy or a game. Research the selling price of each item. Use the coupons below to calculate the best price for each item. Use each coupon only once. Make a collage with pictures of the items and copies of the coupons. Write up your calculations, explain how you found the best price, and include this information with your collage.

Name _____

A Rhyme to Remember

In ancient cultures, before the development and widespread use of written language, storytellers kept the histories of their people alive through generations. Each storyteller passed the stories on to the next storyteller. To make the stories easier to remember and retell, storytellers used songs, chants, and dances in their storytelling. The patterns and rhythms of rhyming words, phrases, and motion made it easier to remember stories and events of the past.

From these oral storytelling traditions came today's music, dances, and cheers. Cheerleaders perform at sporting events and compete in competitions to showcase their skills. Musicians perform concerts and sell recordings of their music for their fans to enjoy.

Your Project **Write and Perform a Cheer or a Rap**

Think about what you have learned about percents in this topic. Write a cheer or a rap that helps you remember the formulas and other math concepts. Then record yourself performing your piece or perform it live for your teacher.

Name _____

Playing Basketball

Basketball players practice jumping, dribbling, passing, and shooting the ball. Their main goal is to get the ball through the hoop. Being tall helps, but posture and balance help as well. When they shoot a basketball, players bend their knees, hold the ball gently, and jump up and forward as they throw. Players who practice the same movement over and over again develop muscle memory. *Muscle memory* means the movement becomes almost automatic, which increases a player's accuracy over time.

Your Project **Estimate Baskets**

Estimate the number of baskets you would make out of 12 shots from the free-throw line. Then estimate the number you would make out of 12 shots from the 3-point line. Attempt 12 of each type of shot. Keep track of the shots you make, and calculate your percent success rate.

How far off were your estimates? Based on each set, estimate the number of baskets you would make out of your next 12 attempts. Repeat the process for three or four more rounds, comparing your success rates by round and by distance.

Make a poster displaying the data from your experiments, including the percent error of your estimates and success rate. Summarize your findings.

Name _____

Pixelated Pictures

The first home video game was released in 1972. Around the same time, the first personal computers were starting to be sold. Throughout the '70s, '80s, and early '90s, graphics technology and screen resolutions were quite limited. As a result, images often had boxy designs in which each pixel was individually visible. A *pixel* is the smallest picture element of a digital screen or image.

In the early 1980s, a woman named Susan Kare became a major influence in the field of computer graphics. She designed some of the original fonts and icons for one of the biggest computer companies of the time. Her black and white icons were all designed on a 32 × 32-pixel grid, which worked within the technological limits of the time.

Since the early 1990s, technology has improved, allowing a greater variety of design styles and more realistic images. The pixelated style still remains in a number of modern games and apps.

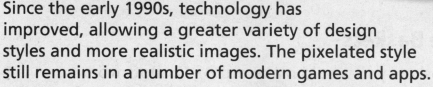

Your Project **Design an App Icon**

Suppose you are a game designer working on a new game app that uses a pixelated style. You decide to design the app icon image using a 32 × 32 grid as a throwback to the older style icons. You want to use at least three colors and do not want any single color used for less than 5 pixels. Each pixel can be only one color.

After you have completed the design of your icon, estimate what percent of the icon is made up of each color. Then calculate the actual percent of each color. What was your percent error?

Write an email to send to the rest of your design team to get their feedback on your design. In your email, include your completed icon design and your color analysis.

Name _____

Analyze Activity Tracker Data
Fitness Trackers

Fitness trackers track a variety of data about the user and their activities.
Different models of fitness trackers track different sorts of data.
If you struggle with your research, try the following phrases to get you started.

- Fitness tracker data
- Fitness tracker comparison
- Average fitness tracker data

- Fitness tracker features
- Pros and cons of fitness trackers
- Accuracy of fitness trackers

Part A Research different fitness trackers. List different types of data that are collected by trackers and complete the table.

Types of Data	Data Unit	Recommended Goal/Range	How Does the Tracker Determine This Data?

Part B Research the pros and cons of fitness trackers.

Pros	Cons

Name _____

Analyze Activity Tracker Data

Design a New Display

Considering what you have learned about fitness trackers, design at least one new data display for the tracker's screen or app that improves on existing displays. At least one display must incorporate the use of percents.

Describe existing displays and how you wish to improve on them.

What type of users will benefit from your new display?

List the requirements for your solution.

Explain the math involved in how the new display calculates the data presented on screen.

Draw a mock-up of your new display.

Name _____

There are 80 animals at an animal shelter. Of those animals, 27.5% are dogs.
How many dogs are at the shelter?

Use equivalent ratios to find 27.5% of 80.

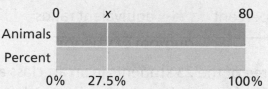

$\frac{27.5}{100} = \frac{x}{80}$

Write equivalent ratios to relate
the percent and number of dogs.

$\frac{27.5}{100} \cdot 80 = \frac{x}{80} \cdot 80$

Multiply both sides by 80.

$x = 22$

Simplify.

There are 22 dogs at the shelter.

Josh and Daniel each want to save $600 to attend a sports camp. Josh has saved 60% of
the amount. Daniel has saved $320. Who has saved more money? How much more?

1. Complete the equivalent ratios to find 60% of $600.

$\frac{\boxed{}}{100} = \frac{x}{\boxed{}}$

2. What number should you multiply both sides by to solve for x?

3. How much money has Josh saved?

4. Who has saved more money? How much more?

On the Back!

5. A total of 150 students voted for class president. Bianca received
   43 votes, and Carlos received 38% of the votes. Which student
   received more votes? How many more?

Name _____

Use the list below to complete the sentences.

percent	equivalent ratios	whole	part

Three of the 25 students in an art class are left-handed. In other words, 12% of the students in the class are left-handed.

1. The number 3 represents _____ of the class.

2. The number 25 represents the _____ class.

3. You can write _____ to represent this situation: $\frac{3}{25} = \frac{12}{100}$.

4. You can also write the _____ of the left-handed students in the class, which is 12%.

For each pair of ratios, circle *equivalent ratios* or *not equivalent ratios*.

5. $\frac{2}{5}$ and $\frac{20}{100}$ equivalent ratios   not equivalent ratios

6. $\frac{3}{6}$ and $\frac{50}{100}$ equivalent ratios   not equivalent ratios

7. $\frac{150}{600}$ and $\frac{40}{100}$ equivalent ratios   not equivalent ratios

Read the word problem below. Then answer the questions to identify the steps for solving the problem.

Aisha and David are reading a book that has 240 pages. Aisha has read 55% of the book. David has read 126 pages. Which student has read more pages so far? How many more pages has that student read?

1. Underline the two questions that you need to answer.

2. Circle the information in the problem about how many pages each student has read.

3. What information do you need to find before you can answer the questions asked in the problem?

4. Complete the diagram and write the equivalent ratios that can help you find the information you identified in Exercise 3.

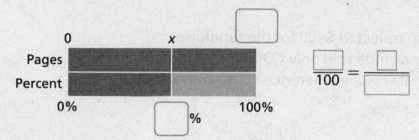

5. After finding the information in Exercise 3, how will you answer the questions asked in the problem?

Name _____

The school band is selling items to raise $9,500 for a trip. For each item sold, the band's profit is a percent of the selling price, as shown in the table.

Band Fundraiser			
Item	CD	Calendar	T-Shirt
Selling Price	$20	$16	$10
Band's Profit	38%	45%	52%

1. Martha has sold 5 CDs, 6 calendars, and 4 T-shirts. How much profit has the band earned from Martha's sales?

2. Of the 24 items that Jamal has sold, 25% are CDs. Jamal has sold 4 more T-shirts than CDs. How much profit has the band earned from Jamal's sales?

3. Bao and Linda have each collected $400 for the fundraiser. Bao sold only T-shirts, and Linda sold only CDs. Which student raised more money? What was the difference in the amounts the students raised?

4. The flutists' goal is to raise 18% of the total amount needed. The trumpeters' goal is 85% of the flutists' goal. If both of these groups meet their goals, which group raised more money? What was the difference in the amounts the students raised?

5. The band raised 112% of its goal. If 40% of the profit came from calendar sales, what was the band's profit from calendar sales?

Name _____

Norah has read 72 pages, which is 45% of a book. How many pages are in the book?

Step 1 Set up the proportion.

$$\frac{\text{part}}{\text{whole}} = \frac{p}{100}$$

$$\frac{72}{w} = \frac{45}{100}$$

Step 2 Solve for the variable.

$$\frac{72}{w} = \frac{45}{100}$$ Write the proportion.

$$\frac{72}{w} \cdot w = \frac{45}{100} \cdot w$$ Multiply each side by w.

$$72 = \frac{45w}{100}$$ Simplify.

$$72 \cdot \frac{100}{45} = \frac{45w}{100} \cdot \frac{100}{45}$$ Multiply by the reciprocal.

$$w = 160$$ Simplify.

There are 160 pages in Norah's book.

Trevon made 24 of the 40 free throws he attempted last season. What percent of his attempted free throws did Trevon make?

1. Complete the proportion. Use a variable for the missing value.

$$\frac{\square}{\square} = \frac{\square}{100}$$

2. Multiply each side of the proportion by _____.

3. Write the equation you can use to solve for the variable.

4. What is the missing value in the proportion?

5. What percent of his attempted free throws did Trevon make?

On the Back!

6. Jason was asked 40 questions on a quiz show. He answered 85% of the questions correctly. How many questions did he answer correctly?

Name _____

**Use the following terms to complete the descriptions below.
Some terms may be used more than once.**

whole	part	proportion	variable

1.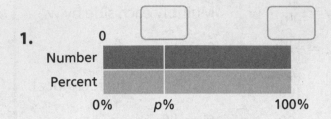

2.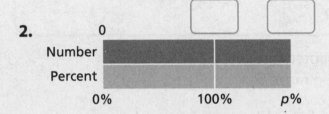

3. In each bar diagram above, the _____ corresponds to
100% and the _____ corresponds to *p*%.

4. When solving percent problems, set up a _____.
For example:

$$\frac{\boxed{}}{\boxed{}} = \frac{p}{100}$$

5. Use a _____ to represent the value you need to find.

Name _____

Review the Key Concept from the lesson. Then answer the questions to help you understand how to read a Key Concept.

KEY CONCEPT

You can use a bar diagram and a proportion to solve different types of percent problems. Use equivalent ratios in a proportion to compare the part to the whole.

$$\frac{n}{w} = \frac{P}{100}$$

Type	Example	Proportion
Find the **PERCENT**.	What percent of 5 is 4?	$\frac{4}{5} = \frac{P}{100}$
Find the **PART**.	What number is 80% of 5?	$\frac{n}{5} = \frac{80}{100}$
Find the **WHOLE**.	4 is 80% of what number?	$\frac{4}{w} = \frac{80}{100}$

1. Circle the numerators in the proportion $\frac{part}{whole} = \frac{p}{100}$. Then circle the corresponding parts of the bar diagram.

2. Draw a square around the denominators in the proportion $\frac{part}{whole} = \frac{p}{100}$. Then draw squares around the corresponding parts in the bar diagram.

3. How is the bar diagram related to the proportion?

4. Look at the second example. Highlight the given values using different colors. Then highlight the corresponding values in the proportion the same color.

5. In all three examples, underline the word "of" and the value that follows it. What part of the proportion is the underlined value in all three examples?

Name _____

Demographers are scientists who study trends in populations, including how the percent of people in different age groups changes over time. The table gives some information about the U.S. population in 2010.

U.S. Population (2010)		
Age group	Number of People (millions)	Percent of Population
Total	308.7	100%
0–17	☐	24.0%
65 and older	40.3	☐ %

1. Complete the table. Express the number of people in millions, rounded to the nearest tenth, and round the percent to the nearest tenth.

2. The number of people in the 0–17 age group is expected to increase by 6.1 million between 2010 and 2030. How many people would you expect to be in this age group in 2030? Can you use this information to predict the percent of the U.S. population that will be in the 0–17 age group in 2030? Explain.

3. Demographers predict that 22.4% of the U.S. population will be in the 0–17 age group in 2030. Write a proportion that you could use to find the predicted total population of the U.S. in 2030. What is the predicted population? Express your answer in millions, rounded to the nearest tenth.

4. Demographers predict that by 2030, the 65 and older age group will include 180.6% as many people as it did in 2010. To the nearest tenth, what percent of the total population is expected to be 65 and older in 2030?

Name _____

A ticket company charges a 4% service fee on all orders. How much is
the service fee for a ticket that costs $65?

Step 1 Write the percent equation.

$$\text{part} = \text{percent} \cdot \text{whole}$$

Step 2 Substitute the given values and use a variable for the missing value.
Write the percent as a decimal.

$$p = 0.04 \cdot 65$$

Step 3 Simplify.

$$p = 2.6$$

The service fee is $2.60.

Xavier downloaded 40 songs last week, including 14 jazz songs. What percent
of Xavier's downloads were jazz songs?

1. Complete the percent equation, using a variable for the missing value.

   $\square = \square \cdot \square$

2. How can you solve the equation for the variable?

3. Solve for the variable.

4. What percent of Xavier's downloads were jazz songs?

On the Back!

5. There are 65 students who walk to West Middle School each day.
   This is 12.5% of the total number of students at the school. How
   many students attend West Middle School?

Name _____

Use each term from the list once to represent the item in each box.

whole	equivalent ratios	decimal
part	commission	percent equation

1. $\frac{part}{whole} = percent$ $part = percent \cdot whole$	**2.** 4% of $3,650 in sales	**3.** $\frac{4}{5} = \frac{80}{100}$
4. 3 of 11 ↑	**5.** 0.03	**6.** 24 of 90 ↑

Name _____

Read the word problem below. Then answer the questions to identify the steps for solving the problem.

The bar diagram shows the amount of data Mara has used for her cell phone plan this month. What percent of the total data is still available for Mara use?

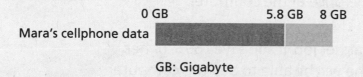

0 GB   5.8 GB   8 GB

Mara's cellphone data

GB: Gigabyte

1. Underline the question that you need to answer.

2. What information is represented by the bar diagram?

3. Circle the part of the bar diagram that represents the unknown percent.

4. What information do you need to find before you can answer the question asked in the problem?

5. How can you find the information you identified in Exercise 4?

6. Once you have found the information in Exercise 4, what equation can you use to solve the problem?

Name _____

Miranda is saving money to buy a new computer that costs
$900. She estimates that it will take her three months working at
her part-time job to save enough money for the computer.

1. Including sales tax, the total amount Miranda must save is
   $964.80. Miranda will need to pay $_____ in sales tax,
   which is _____% of the price of the computer.

2. Miranda earns $12 per hour at her job. If she saves 60% of her
   earnings for the computer, she will be able to buy the computer
   after working _____ hours at her job.

3. In the first month, Miranda worked 33.5 hours. Of the total amount
   she needs to save for the computer, what percent did she save in
   the first month? Describe two different ways to find the answer.

4. In the second month, Miranda received a $135 check from her
   grandmother. This was 75% of the amount Miranda saved from her job
   in that month. How many hours did Miranda work during the second
   month? How much money has she saved so far? Explain your answers.

5. At the end of the third month, the electronics store announces a
   sale. The computer's price will be discounted 15%. For how many
   hours must Miranda work to save enough money to buy the
   computer at the end of the third month? Explain your answer.

Name _____

Percent change describes an amount of change as a percent of the original value.

change = percent change • original amount

Last year, Billy was 48 inches tall. This year, he is 54 inches tall. What is the percent increase in Billy's height?

p%

amount of change

original amount

100%

Step 1 Find the amount of change. $54 - 48 = 6$

Step 2 Use the percent equation. $6 = p \cdot 48$

$$\frac{6}{48} = \frac{p \cdot 48}{48}$$

$$\frac{6}{48} = p$$

$$0.125 = p$$

Rewrite the decimal as a percent. Billy's height has increased by 12.5%.

Percent error describes the difference between an estimated value and the actual value as a percent of the actual value.

difference = percent error • actual value

Jason predicted that 227 students would attend the school dance. The actual number was 250. What is the percent error of Jason's prediction?

1. What is the difference between the predicted value and the actual value?

2. Complete the equation: [   ] $= p \cdot$ [   ]

3. Solve the equation for *p*.

4. What is the percent error?

On the Back!

5. Last week, there were 420 new subscribers to a Web site. This week, the number of new subscribers decreased by 5%. How many new subscribers are there this week?

Name _____

Use each of these words once to complete the sentences.

percent change	percent error

1. A _____ describes the accuracy of an estimated value as compared to an actual value.

2. The _____ describes how much a quantity has changed when compared to its original amount.

Read each scenario. Then choose whether you would find the *percent increase*, *percent decrease*, or *percent error*.

3. Yesterday, I ran 5 miles. Today, I ran 3.7 miles.

   percent increase   percent decrease   percent error

4. The marching band had 304 students last year. This year, 322 students participate in band.

   percent increase   percent decrease   percent error

5. Tomas estimated there were 125 people in the audience. There were actually 137 people.

   percent increase   percent decrease   percent error

6. A town's population was 36,067 in 2005. Ten years later, the population is 37,902.

   percent increase   percent decrease   percent error

7. A faulty scale displayed the weight of the package as 14 pounds 13 ounces. The exact weight was 13 pounds 6 ounces.

   percent increase   percent decrease   percent error

Name _____

Read the word problem below. Then answer the questions to identify the steps for solving the problem.

Last year, 625 students attended Diego's school. This year, 590 students attend the school. What is the percent change?

1. Is the percent change an increase or a decrease? Explain.

2. To find the percent change, you can use the following equation:

   amount of change = percent change • original amount

   $$\frac{\text{amount of change}}{\text{original amount}} = \frac{\text{percent change} \cdot \text{original amount}}{\text{original amount}}$$

   $$\frac{\text{amount of change}}{\text{original amount}} = \text{percent change}$$

   In the problem above, circle the original amount. Underline the new value.

3. Is the amount of change given in the problem? If so, draw a box around it. If not, describe how you can find it.

4. After solving the equation for percent change, what form will the answer be in? What additional step is needed to find the final answer?

Name _____

The table shows the total number of U.S. participants in four high school sports over several school years.

	2012–2013	2013–2014	2014–2015
Archery	2,647	4,867	7,744
Basketball	971,796	974,398	970,983
Cross Country	463,569	470,668	472,597
Soccer	782,514	791,983	808,250

1. Rounded to the nearest tenth, what was the percent decrease in basketball participants from 2013–2014 to 2014–2015?

2. Which sport had the greatest percent increase from 2012–2013 to 2014–2015? What was this percent increase to the nearest tenth?

3. In 2013–2014, 46.3% of cross-country participants were girls. The number of girls who participated in cross-country increased by 1.6% from 2013–2014 to 2014–2015. To the nearest tenth, what percent of 2014–2015 cross-country participants were girls?

4. In 2012–2013, there were 1,158 more archery participants than in 2011–2012. To the nearest tenth, what was the percent increase in archery participants from 2011–2012 to 2012–2013?

5. Suppose the number of girls who play soccer in 2015–2016 increases by 2.3% as compared to 2014–2015, while the number of boys who play soccer decreases by 2.3% during the same time. Can you tell whether the total number of soccer players will increase, decrease, or remain the same? Explain how you would know.

Name _____

A tent that usually sells for $220 is on sale for 15% off. What is the sale price?

Step 1 Find the markdown amount.

markdown = percent markdown • original price

$\qquad m = 0.15 \cdot 220$

$\qquad m = 33$

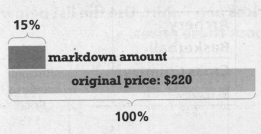

Step 2 Find the sale price.

sale price = original price – markdown

$\qquad s = 220 - 33$

$\qquad s = 187$

The sale price is $187.

Use similar reasoning to find a markup amount. The markup is the amount of increase from the original price to the selling price.   markup = percent markup • cost

Marcy has $20. She wants to buy a book that is marked down 30% from its original price of $28. If the sales tax is 2.5%, does Marcy have enough money to buy the book?

1. Complete the percent equation to find the markdown.

$m = \boxed{} \cdot \boxed{}$

$ = \boxed{}$

2. Complete the equation to find the sale price.

$s = \boxed{} - \boxed{}$

$ = \boxed{}$

3. How much is the sales tax on the price you found in Exercise 2?
    Add the sale price and the sales tax to find the total cost of the book.

4. Does Marcy have enough money to buy the book? Explain.

On the Back!

5. The school store buys granola bars for $0.40 each and sells them
    for $0.65. What is the percent markup?

The *wholesale price* is the amount a store pays for an item before selling that item to a customer. The diagram below shows the prices of a T-shirt. Use the list below to complete the sentences about these prices.

plus	discounted sale price	percent markdown
wholesale price	percent markup	markdown amount
markup amount	regular selling price	minus

1. The regular selling price includes a markup from the

   _____.

2. If the wholesale price is $10, the 50% _____ is $5.

3. The _____ from the wholesale price to the regular selling price is 50%.

4. A customer's cost for the T-shirt is the wholesale price _____ the 50% markup.

5. During a sale, the T-shirt price is a markdown from the

   _____.

6. The _____ from the regular selling price to the discounted sale price is $3.

7. The _____ from the regular selling price to the discounted sale price is 20%.

8. The discounted sale price for the T-shirt is the regular selling price _____ the 20% markdown.

9. Marked down 20% from the regular selling price, the _____ of the T-shirt is $12.

**Read the word problem below. Then answer the questions to
identify the steps for solving the problem.**

A pair of shoes had an original price of $80. The shoes are now on sale
for 35% off. What is the sale price of the shoes?

1. Circle the words in the problem that tell whether this is a
    markdown or markup.

2. Complete the bar diagram to represent this problem.

3. Draw an arrow toward the part of the bar diagram that represents
    the answer to the problem.

4. After a sale of _____% off, the final price is _____% of the original
    price of the shoes.

5. What unit will the answer be in?

6. Describe a reasonable answer to this problem. Explain your
    reasoning.

Name _____

An electronics store is having a progressive sale. In this type of sale, the price of an item is marked down each day by a percent of the previous day's price. The percent markdown is the same from one day to the next. The graph shows the price of a particular television set over several days. The price for Day 0 is the original price of the television.

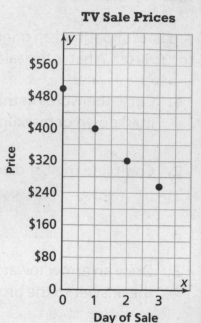

TV Sale Prices

1. By what percent is the television's price marked down each day?

2. A customer bought this model of television at a price of $163.84. On what day of the sale did the customer buy the television?

3. How do you know that the points of the graph do not represent a linear relationship?

4. What is the percent markdown from the original price to the sale price on Day 3 of the sale?

5. The store manager asks an employee to design a display sign for a camera that will be marked down 10% in price each day. The manager has not yet noticed an error in the sign. Describe the error in the sign and explain what will happen on the tenth day of the sale if the sign is not changed and the pattern continues.

Camera Sale!

Monday: 10% off
Tuesday: 20% off
Wednesday: 30% off
Thursday: 40% off
Friday: 50% off

Darius deposits $600 into a simple interest savings account. After a year, the account balance will be $615. What is the interest rate?

Step 1 Find the interest earned in one year.

$615 - 600 = 15$

Step 2 Use the percent equation.

interest amount = initial deposit • interest rate

$15 = 600 \cdot r$	Substitute.
$15 = 600r$	Simplify.
$\dfrac{15}{600} = \dfrac{600r}{600}$	Divide both sides by 600.
$r = 0.025$	Simplify to find the interest rate as a decimal.

The simple interest rate is 2.5%.

Enrique earned $101.40 in interest over 6 years in a savings account that pays 1.3% simple interest per year. How much did Enrique originally deposit?

1. What was the amount of interest earned in one year? Explain how you found your answer.

2. Complete the percent equation below to find how much Enrique initially deposited. Use the interest amount you found in Exercise 1.

   interest amount = [_____] • initial deposit

   [____] = [____] • initial deposit

   [____] = initial deposit

On the Back!

3. Tony's deposit earned $40.80 in simple interest over 3 years in an account with an interest rate of 1.7%. How much did Tony deposit?

Name _____

**Use the list to complete the table, equation, and sentences.
Some terms might be used more than once.**

interest rate	principal	interest

Term	Definition
	The initial amount of money
	The amount of money that is earned on a deposit
	A percent used to calculate interest on a principal

Equation

_____ = _____ × interest rate

Sentences

Owen deposits $300 in a savings account that earns 1.7% interest each year.

The _____ of the savings account is $300.

The _____ of the savings account is 1.7%.

The _____ earned after the first year is 0.017 · 300 = 5.1, or $5.10.

Match each interest rate with its decimal equivalent.

1. 3.5%   0.035

2. 0.35%   0.0305

3. 3.05%   0.0035

Name _____

**Read the word problem below. Then answer the questions to
identify the steps for solving the problem.**

Vinnie's savings account earns simple interest each year. His initial
deposit was $800, and after 5 years, the balance is $848. What is the
interest rate?

1. Underline the question that you need to answer. What form will
    the correct answer be in?

2. Highlight the information that you need to solve the problem.

3. The following steps that you can use to solve the problem are not
    in order. Write a number from 1 to 4 in each box to indicate the
    correct order of the steps.

    ☐ Find the amount of interest earned each year.

    ☐ Express the interest rate as a percent.

    ☐ Find the interest rate as a decimal.

    ☐ Find the total amount of interest earned.

4. Without doing any calculations, describe how to find the total
    amount of interest earned and the amount of interest earned
    each year.

5. Explain the steps you can take to check your answer.

Name _____

A bank offers three different savings accounts.

Account Type	Minimum Initial Deposit	Annual Simple Interest Rate
Basic Savings	$0	0.8%
Super Savings	$500	1.1%
Deluxe Savings	$5000	1.5%

1. Samir opened a Super Savings account with an initial deposit of $620. He did not make any additional deposits. What is his account balance after 3 years?

2. Beth and Reena opened Basic Savings accounts on the same day. Reena's initial deposit was twice as much as Beth's. After 5 years, their combined interest earned was $21.00. What was the amount of Reena's initial deposit?

3. Another bank offers 1.9% annual simple interest for deposits of $10,000 or more. Carter opened an account at this bank with an initial deposit of $12,000. Ruth opened a Deluxe Savings account that same day. If they have both earned the same amount in interest after one year, what was the amount of Ruth's initial deposit?

4. Make a graph that shows the annual balance of a Super Savings account opened with an initial deposit of $500, assuming no additional deposits or withdrawals are made.

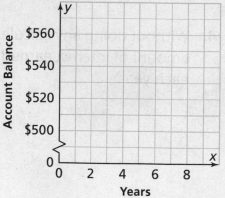

5. How would the graph be different for an initial deposit greater than $500? How would the graph be different for a Basic Savings account? Explain.

Name _____

Generate Equivalent Expressions

Dear Family,

Your child is learning to work with algebraic expressions. He or she will learn to write and evaluate expressions and to write equivalent expressions. Your child will also learn how to write and interpret expressions that represent real-world situations.

Here is an activity you can do with your child to help him or her become more comfortable with algebraic expressions.

Express It!

Take turns with your child writing algebraic expressions that represent real-world situations. For example, if a child is x years old, the expression that represents the age of a cousin who is 5 years older is $x + 5$. If a family's rent is y dollars per month, what expression represents the total rent for one year? After you have written an expression, discuss how you might use it to solve problems. For example, how could you use the expression for your age to find how old you will be when your child graduates from high school?

Observe Your Child

Focus on Mathematical Practices
Look for and make use of structure.

Help your child become proficient with this Mathematical Practice. Have him or her explain the real-world meaning of each part of the expressions.

Generar expresiones equivalentes

Estimada familia:

Su hijo o hija está aprendiendo a trabajar con expresiones algebraicas. Aprenderá a escribir expresiones y evaluarlas, y a escribir expresiones equivalentes. También está aprendiendo a escribir e interpretar expresiones que representan situaciones de la vida diaria.

Esta es una actividad que puede realizar con su hijo o hija como ayuda para que pueda sentirse más cómodo con las expresiones algebraicas.

¡Exprésalo!

Túrnese con su hijo o hija para escribir expresiones algebraicas que representen situaciones de la vida diaria. Por ejemplo, si un hijo tiene x años, la expresión que representa la edad de un primo que es 5 años mayor es $x + 5$. Si el alquiler que debe pagar una familia es de y dólares por mes, ¿qué expresión representa el total de dinero para el alquiler de un año? Después de escribir una expresión, comenten cómo podrían usarla para resolver problemas. Por ejemplo, ¿cómo pueden usar la expresión de la edad que tiene usted para hallar la edad que tendrá su hijo o hija al graduarse de la preparatoria?

Observe a su hijo o hija

Enfoque en las Prácticas matemáticas
Buscar y utilizar la estructura.

Ayude a su hijo o hija a adquirir competencia en esta Práctica matemática. Pídale que explique qué representa cada parte de las expresiones en la vida diaria.

Name _____

Expressive Expressions

Many people use emojis in typed communication. Before there were emojis, *emoticons* were widely used. Emoticons use a combination of punctuation marks to look like different facial expressions. Most emoticons used in the United States require tilting your head to see the facial expressions. The first emoticons originated in late 1982, around the time the internet was being established, and quickly expanded to include a wide variety of expressions and symbols. Emoticons were an essential part of early netspeak and are still used today.

The use of emoticons was gradually overtaken by the more graphic images known as emojis. The earliest emoji sets were developed in Japan in the late 1990s. Emojis became widely available in the United States in late 2010, when over 700 emojis were added to the Unicode Standard. By 2018, nearly 3,000 emojis had been added to the Unicode Standard.

:-(:-)

:-P   :-[

;-)   :-D

{o,o}
/)__)
 " "

Your Project **Write and Illustrate a Children's Book**

Write and illustrate a children's book called *Expressive Expressions*. In your book, use emojis to represent unknown values to show what you have learned in this topic about expressions. Demonstrate different ways to generate equivalent expressions. Your story should involve simplifying, factoring, adding, subtracting, and expanding expressions.

Name _____

Guaranteed Equivalence

There are many ways to use coins to represent $1.00. While it's fairly easy to tell that the coins on the left are equivalent to $1.00, it's not immediately clear that the coins on the right are equivalent to $1.00. (They are.)

Algebraic expressions can be equivalent, as well. Compare the expression $3x - \frac{1}{2}y - 0.7$ to the expressions below. Guess what? They are all equivalent. You can test for equivalence by substituting for x and for y into any of the expressions and simplifying. Just make sure you use a consistent value for x and a consistent value for y in all of the expressions.

$$3x - \frac{1}{2}y - 0.7$$

$$-\frac{1}{3}(-9x + 1.5y) - \frac{7}{10}$$

$$\frac{1}{2}(6x - y - 1\frac{4}{10})$$

$$\frac{1}{10}(30x - 5y - 7)$$

$$6x - \frac{3}{2}y - \frac{7}{10} - 3x + y$$

Your Project **Generate Equivalence**

Write an algebraic expression for a real-world situation. Use at least two variables with coefficients, and include one fraction and one decimal in your expression. Find ten expressions that look different from your expression but are equivalent to it. Make a poster showing all your expressions and how they are equivalent.

Songwriting

Writing a song is like writing a story. Songwriters want to engage the listener in what they have to say and how they say it. Some songwriters begin by thinking of a melody in their head or by deciding on a theme, while others write the lyrics first, and then set them to music. Then songwriters write a rough draft of the music and the lyrics, remembering to include verses and a chorus. Some songwriters bounce ideas off friends, as well. They may even write songs for other people to play and record.

Your Project **Write a Song**

Write song lyrics about what you learned in this topic. Each verse should be about a specific idea from the topic, and the chorus should tie the verses together. Include examples of equivalent expressions, and include lyrics on how to determine whether two expressions are equivalent. Set your lyrics to music. Choose your favorite song and use that music or write your own music. Record a video of yourself singing your song.

Name _____

The Perfect Playground

Designing a playground requires planning and knowledge of the surrounding community. A playground can be a simple collection of play structures, or it can be built with a specific theme in mind, such as castles, spaceships, or safaris. The layout of the playground is important. Designers have to take into consideration children's well-being and safety, such as the number of children moving through the playground, in order to avoid congestion and collisions. Easy access to restrooms and drinking fountains are also important details. A playground must be designed to fit the space available and to provide the best possible environment for children.

Your Project **Build a Model Playground**

An empty lot with a width of 51.5 feet and a length of 30 feet has been approved for the development of a new playground. You are able to increase the length of playground by clearing some debris behind the lot. Write an expression to represent the total area of the playground. Be sure your expression accounts for the unknown amount of space you will gain by clearing debris.

Sketch a design for your playground. Split the lot into four sections using one vertical line and one horizontal line. Write an expression to represent the area of each section.

Make a model of your playground and the equipment that will be in each section. Use what you have learned about expressions to describe each section.

P-5D

Analyze Activity Tracker Data

Fitness Tracker Sensors

Fitness trackers collect data from their users in a variety of ways.

Part A Research the different types of sensors used for data collection in fitness trackers and how those sensors work.

Type of Sensor	How It Works

Part B Some of the data collected from the fitness tracker is input into formulas to calculate other information. Brainstorm or research what types of data the fitness tracker engineers might use formulas to calculate.

Analyze Activity Tracker Data

Fitness Tracker Accuracy

Different fitness trackers use different formulas to interpret the data recorded by the sensors in the device. This results in small inaccuracies of data collection.

Method 1 If you have access to multiple fitness trackers, wear multiple trackers at once for a set period of time. Compare the different types of data from each tracker in the table below.

Method 2 If you do not have access to different fitness trackers, search for data online from other users who have performed similar tests to that in Method 1. If you need help finding information, try searching for "fitness tracker accuracy" or "average fitness tracker data." Look one of the following types of data to complete the table below:

- Data that compares multiple types of data from several fitness trackers
- Data that compares one type of data from several fitness trackers over multiple days

Type of Tracker	Select one title: **Types of Data** or **Dates of Data Collection**			
	_____	_____	_____	_____

1. Look at the table. What trends do you notice?

2. Considering what you have learned about trackers so far, what would you recommend to improve their accuracy?

Name _____

Analyze Activity Tracker Data

Tracking Fitness Goals

Many people use fitness trackers to help them achieve specific fitness goals.

Three fitness goals are listed below. Complete the table by adding additional fitness goals, and a formula that fitness tracking companies can use to calculate how close the user is to achieving the goal, and explain how that formula would work.

Fitness Goal	Formula	Explanation of Formula
Walk 10,000 steps per day		
Walk 5 miles per day		
Be active for 60 minutes per day		

Name _____

Analyze Activity Tracker Data

Design a New Display

Design a display for at least two of your goals from the Tracking Fitness Goals sheet. Each fitness goal should display the data in a different way.

1	Describe existing displays and how you wish to improve on them.
	What type of users will benefit from your new display?
	List the requirements for your solution.
	Explain the math involved in how the new display calculates the data presented on screen.
	Draw a mock-up of your new display.

Analyze Activity Tracker Data

Design a New Display, *continued*

2	Describe existing displays and how you wish to improve on them.
	What type of users will benefit from your new display?
	List the requirements for your solution.
	Explain the math involved in how the new display calculates the data presented on screen.
	Draw a mock-up of your new display.

Amber is saving money to buy a bicycle. She saves $60 her grandfather gave her, and plans to save an additional $5 each week. How much will Amber save after *w* weeks?

Use a bar diagram to represent the amount Amber will save after *w* weeks.

Amber will save 60 + 5*w* dollars after *w* weeks.

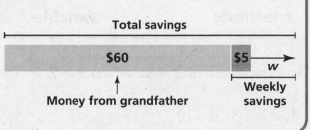

Total savings

$60 $5   *w*

Money from grandfather   Weekly savings

Reggie drives 10 miles from the airport to the highway. Once on the highway, he drives at a speed of 55 miles per hour. What is Reggie's total distance from the airport *h* hours after reaching the highway?

1. Complete the bar diagram.

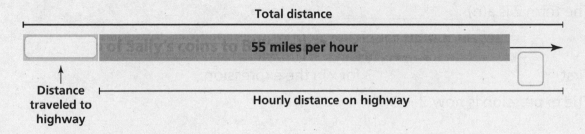

Total distance

55 miles per hour

Distance traveled to highway

Hourly distance on highway

2. Write an expression that represents the distance that Reggie travels on the highway in *h* hours.

3. Write an expression that represents Reggie's total distance from the airport *h* hours after reaching the highway.

On the Back!

4. Chrissy had 4 gallons of gas in her tank when she arrived at the gas station. She pumped gas into her car at a rate of $\frac{3}{10}$ gallon per second. How many gallons of gas were in the tank after *s* seconds?

Name _____

Use each of these words once to complete the sentences.

coefficient	expression	simplify
substitute	variable	constant

Find the value of $2 - 3x$ when $x = 7$.

1. $2 - 3x$ is a(n) _____ .

2. The term $3x$ contains both a(n) _____ and a(n) _____ .

3. The term 2 is a(n) _____ term.

4. First, _____ 3 for x in the expression.
   The expression is now $2 - 3(7)$.

5. To solve the problem, _____ $2 - 3(7)$.
   The expression $2 - 3x$ is equivalent to $2 - 3(7) = 2 - 21 = -19$
   when $x = 7$.

Tell whether each of the following is an *expression* or *not an expression*.

6. 15

   expression   not an expression

7. $x + 5 = 8$

   expression   not an expression

8. $5x - 3y + 0.25$

   expression   not an expression

Name _____

**Read the word problem below. Then answer the questions
to help you understand the problem.**

Ben wants to buy a binder and some pencils from the school store.
Binders cost $2.25 each and pencils cost $0.75 each. How much will
it cost Ben to buy 1 binder and *p* pencils?

1. Underline the question you need to answer.

2. Circle the information about the price of binders.

3. What operation will Ben use to find his total cost at the school
    store? Explain.

4. Circle the expression that represents the total cost of the pencils
    Ben will buy.

    $2.50p $2.50 + $0.75p

    $7.75 − $0.75p $0.75p

5. What type of answer will this problem have? Explain.

A soccer team uses 5-gallon coolers to hold water during games and practices. Each cooler holds 640 fluid ounces. The team has small cups that each hold 6.25 fluid ounces and large cups that each hold 8.75 fluid ounces.

1. The team fills *c* coolers for practice. During practice, the players pour *s* small cups and *g* large cups of water. Write an expression that represents the amount of water that remains in the coolers.

2. Draw a bar diagram to represent the situation.

3. Write and evaluate an expression to represent how much water will be left if the team fills 3 coolers and then pours 40 small cups and 60 large cups.

4. Write an expression to represent how much water will be left if the team fills 2 coolers and then pours 85 small cups and an unknown number of large cups. Explain how you can use your expression from Exercise 1 to answer this question.

5. Write an expression that the team can use to find the number of coolers needed to fill *s* small cups and *g* large cups. Explain how you wrote your expression.

You can use properties to show that the expressions
$3x - 3$ and $-3 + 3x$ are equivalent.

$3x - 3 = 3x + (-3)$ Additive Inverse
$\qquad = -3 + 3x$ Commutative Property

Equivalent expressions have the same value for all values of the variable.

x	3x − 3	−3 + 3x
1	$3(1) - 3 = 0$	$-3 + 3(1) = 0$
2	$3(2) - 3 = 3$	$-3 + 3(2) = 3$
3	$3(3) - 3 = 6$	$-3 + 3(3) = 6$
4	$3(4) - 3 = 9$	$-3 + 3(4) = 9$

A cup of tea costs $3 at a local cafe. Alan and his wife, Patty, have a coupon for $1 off their order. Alan says the expression $3t - 1$ represents the cost for t cups of tea. Patty says the expression $3t + (-1)$ represents the cost. Are their expressions equivalent? Explain.

1. Use the additive inverse to write an equivalent expression for $3t - 1$.

2. Complete the tables.

Alan's Expression

t	3t − 1	Total Cost
1	$3(1) - 1$	2
2	$3(\square) - 1$	$\square$
3	$3(\square) - 1$	$\square$
4	$3(\square) - 1$	$\square$

Patty's Expression

t	3t + (−1)	Total Cost
1	$3(\square) + (-1)$	$\square$
2	$3(\square) + (-1)$	$\square$
3	$3(\square) + (-1)$	$\square$
4	$3(\square) + (-1)$	$\square$

3. Are Alan's and Patty's expressions equivalent? Explain.

On the Back!

4. Karina bought 8 bagels and used a gift certificate for $4. Her total cost is represented by the expression $8b - 4$, where b is the cost of a bagel. What is an equivalent expression?

Name _____

Choose the term from the list that the equation in each box illustrates.
You will use each term more than once.

Associative Property	additive inverse	Commutative Property

1. $5 + 9 = 9 + 5$	**2.** $x - 7 = x + (-7)$	**3.** $(2a + 1) + 4$ $= 2a + (1 + 4)$
4. $\frac{1}{4}x + (-4) = \frac{1}{4}x - 4$	**5.** $(-2 + x) + (-5y)$ $= (-2) + (x + (-5y))$	**6.** $(x + 2y) + 3$ $= (2y + x) + 3$
7. $(x + (-1)) + 2x$ $= (x - 1) + 2x$	**8.** $3x + (-y) + 1$ $= 3x + (-y + 1)$	**9.** $(-4) + 7x + (-2y)$ $= (-4) + (-2y) + 7x$

Name _____

**Read the word problem below. Then answer the questions to
help you understand the problem.**

Lucy works at a restaurant. One day, she earns $16 per hour when she
cooks for x hours and $14 per hour when she cleans for y hours after she
finishes cooking. Then she eats lunch at the restaurant, which results in
$3.50 being subtracted from her pay. The expression $(16x + 14y) - 3.50$
represents her earnings on this particular day. Use the Commutative and
Associative Properties to write two equivalent expressions.

1. Circle the expression shown in the problem.

2. Underline the properties you will use.

3. If you write one expression as your answer, have you correctly
   solved this problem? Explain.

4. Describe the Commutative Property using words. Write an
   equation that shows the Commutative Property.

5. Describe the Associative Property using words. Write an equation
   that shows the Associative Property.

Name _____

A teacher wrote an algebraic expression on the board and asked students to write an equivalent expression. The teacher's expression is partially shown below.

$$\left(5a + \square\right) + \left(\tfrac{1}{10}c + \square d\right) - 4$$

1. Inez wrote: $-4 + \left(\tfrac{1}{10}c + 11d\right)$. Manny wrote:

   $4 - \left(11d + \tfrac{1}{10}c\right)$. Explain why both students cannot be correct.

2. Trevor wrote: $(10c - 4) + 11d$. What properties did Trevor use? Can he be correct? Explain.

3. Nicole received full credit for her expression: $(11d + (-4)) + 0.1c$. Did either Inez or Manny also receive full credit? If so, whom? If not, explain why.

4. Jeremy wrote a different expression that received full credit. What expression might he have written?

Simplify the expression $9 - 2x - 7 + 4x$.

Step 1 Use the Commutative
Property to reorder the terms
so that like terms are together.

$$9 + 4x - 7 - 2x = 9 - 7 + 4x - 2x$$

Step 2 Use the Associative
Property to group like terms.

$$= (9 - 7) + (4x - 2x)$$

Step 3 Simplify by combining
like terms.

$$= 2 + 2x$$

Eloise's math tutor used algebra tiles to model $3n + 4 - n + 5$. What is the simplified form of this expression?

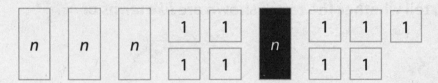

1. Eloise rearranged the tiles as shown below. What property did she use? Write an expression that represents Eloise's arrangement of the tiles.

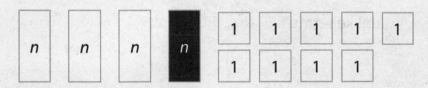

2. Rewrite your expression from Exercise 1 by grouping like terms.

3. What is the simplified form of the expression?

On the Back!

4. What is the simplified form of the expression $7r - 8r + 13 - 2r + 5$?

Name _____

Use the list below to complete the sentences.

constants	variables	simplify

1. You can combine like terms to _____ an expression.

2. All _____ are like terms and can be combined.

3. Terms with the same _____ are considered like terms.

For each of the following, tell whether the terms shown are *like terms* or *unlike terms*.

4. $-5x, -5, 0.5x$

   like terms   unlike terms

5. $63, 19.2, -1$

   like terms   unlike terms

6. $16a, -a, \frac{1}{10}a$

   like terms   unlike terms

7. $5z, 5x, 5y$

   like terms   unlike terms

Name _____

**Read the problem below. Then answer the questions to
identify the steps for solving the problem.**

Simplify the expression $7a + 3 + (-2b) + 5 + (-9a) + 11b$.

1. What does it mean to simplify an expression?

2. Underline the expression in the problem.

3. Complete the table to identify and organize the like terms
   and constant terms in the expression.

Like terms containing a	Like terms containing b	Constant terms
☐	☐	☐
☐	☐	☐

4. What operation will you perform on the terms in the table? Will
   this operation be performed on terms in the same row or the
   same column?

5. How will you know when you have completely solved
   the problem?

Name _____

The diagram below represents the carpeted section of a children's library. The dashed lines divide the carpeted section into 3 regions. All dimensions are in feet.

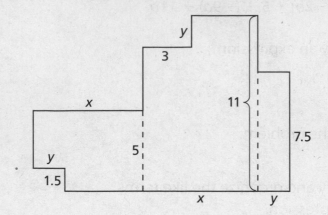

1. Write expressions to represent the area of each carpeted region. For example, the left region is a rectangle whose area is 5x with another rectangle "cut out" whose area is 1.5y. So the area of the left region is $(5x - 1.5y)$ ft^2. Using a similar method, what are the areas of the middle region and right region?

2. Write an expression to represent the total area of the carpeted section. Then, simplify your expression by combining like terms. Include units in your answer.

3. Write an expression for the perimeter of the carpeted section. Simplify your expression by combining like terms. Include units in your answer.

4. If $x = 12$ and the area of the right region is 15 ft^2, what is the total perimeter of the room?

Name _____

You can use the Distributive Property to expand expressions.

$3(7x + 5) = (3)(7x) + (3)(5)$ Use the Distributive Property.
       $= 21x + 15$ Simplify.

The expanded form of $3(7x + 5)$ is $21x + 15$.

The Bains' house has a deck next to the living room. What is the total combined area of the living room and deck?

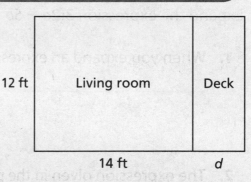

1. The deck and living room combine to form a rectangle. What is the rectangle's width?

2. Write an expression to represent the combined length of the rectangle.

3. Write an expression to represent the combined area of the living room and deck.

4. Use the Distributive Property to expand the product and then simplify. What expression represents the total combined area of the living room and deck?

On the Back!

5. The deli's lunch special offers customers half off the total cost of a sandwich of their choice and a bag of pretzels. The original price of the pretzels is $1.50. Let s represent the original cost of a selected customer's sandwich. What is the total cost of the customer's order?

Name _____

Use the list below to complete the sentences.

like terms	**Distributive Property**	multiply
product of two factors	**equivalent expression**	sign

Expand the expression $3(2a - 5b + 1)$.

1. When you expand an expression, you write a(n)

   _____ .

2. The expression given in the problem is a(n)

   _____ .

3. To expand this expression, use the

   _____ .

4. _____ the factor outside the parentheses by
   each term inside the parentheses.

5. Make sure to consider the _____ of each term in
   all calculations.

6. If possible, combine _____ to simplify
   the expression.

Name _____

**Read the word problem below. Then answer the questions to
help you understand the problem.**

Kira earns $12 per hour at her job. She also earns $10 each day walking
her neighbor's dog. She has decided to save one-fourth of all of the
money she earns for college. The expression $\frac{1}{4}(12x + 10)$ represents the
amount of money Kira saves for college in a day that she works x hours.
Use the Distributive Property to write an equivalent expression.

1. Highlight the sentence that tells what you need to do to solve the
   problem.

2. Circle the expression given in the problem.

3. Underline the words that explain the real-world meaning of the
   expression. Is it necessary to translate the words you underlined into
   a mathematical expression in order to solve the problem? Explain.

4. Explain how you can check if you have written an equivalent
   expression.

Name _____

Martha makes the following fruit punch recipe for an upcoming school party.

> ## Fruit Punch
>
> ☐ pineapple juice
> ☐ cranberry juice
> ☐ lemon-lime soda: 5 fewer cups than pineapple juice
> ☐ orange juice: twice as much as pineapple juice

1. Last time Martha made fruit punch, she used x cups of pineapple juice and y cups of cranberry juice. What expression represents the total number of cups of punch Martha made?
   Write your answer in simplified form.

2. How many more cups of orange juice than lemon-lime soda were in Martha's fruit punch the last time?

3. Last time, Martha filled 12 pitchers with the fruit punch. If she distributed the punch evenly, what expression represents the number of cups in each pitcher? Expand the expression using the Distributive Property and simplify your answer.

4. At the end of the party, Martha had 1.5 pitchers of fruit punch remaining. Write an expression to represent the number of cups of fruit punch remaining, then expand the expression using the Distributive Property and simplify your answer.

Name _____

Factor the expression $6x + 9$.

$6x + 9 = (3 \cdot 2x) + (3 \cdot 3)$ The Greatest Common Factor (GCF) of $6x$ and 9 is 3.
$\quad\quad\; = 3(2x + 3)$ Distributive Property

A room that is 5 meters long has an area
of $5x + 10$ square meters. What expression
represents the width of the room?

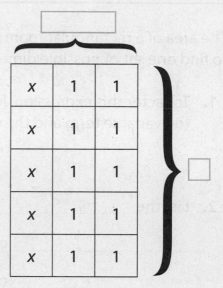

1. What is the GCF of $5x$ and 10?

2. Fill in the box to rewrite the expression $5x + 10$
   using the GCF.

   $5x + 10 = (\boxed{} \cdot x) + (5 \cdot \boxed{})$

3. Use the Distributive Property rewrite the expression from
   Exercise 2 in factored form.

4. What expression represents the width of the room?

5. Label the length and width of the room on the area model.

On the Back!

6. Cameron combined peanuts, cashews, and walnuts to make a trail
   mix. The expression $16p + 24c + 32w$ represents the total number
   of nuts in the mix. Cameron wants to divide the trail mix into equal
   servings, but he does not know how many. Use factoring to write
   expressions that will help Cameron divide the trail mix into
   4 servings or 8 servings.

Name ___________________________________

Additional Vocabulary Support

5-5

Use the list below to complete the sentences.

greatest common factor	**product of two terms**	**factors**
coefficient	**Distributive Property**	**GCF**

The area of a rectangular room is given by the expression $20x - 32$. Factor the expression to find one set of possible dimensions of the room.

1. To factor this expression, look at the ____________________ of the variable term and the constant term.

2. List the ____________________ of 20 and 32.

____________________ of 20: 1, 2, 4, 5, 10, 20

____________________ of 32: 1, 2, 4, 8, 16, 32

3. Circle the greatest factor that appears in both lists. This number is the ______________________________, which is also called the ____________________.

4. Use the ______________________________ to rewrite the expression.

$20x - 32 = 4(5x - 8)$

5. After factoring, the expression is written as a ______________________________.

Name _____

**Read the problem below. Then answer the questions to
identify the steps for solving the problem.**

Hector factored the expression $22x + 33y$ as $11(2x + 3y)$. Is Hector correct?
If he is, show that his answer is correct. If not, factor the expression correctly.

1. Circle the question you are asked to answer.

2. After you determine the answer to the first question, how many
    more steps do you need to complete to finish the problem?
    Underline the step(s).

3. What property is needed to check Hector's answer?

4. Which of the following might help you answer the first question?
    Select all that apply.

    ☐ List all factors of 22 and 33.

    ☐ Add $22x$ and $33y$.

    ☐ Expand $11(2x + 3y)$ using the Distributive Property.

    ☐ List all factors of 11.

5. How can you tell if Hector has answered this problem completely?

Name _____

A fitness center has several rectangular rooms where exercise classes are held.

1. The area of Room A is $27x - 18$ square units. What are possible dimensions of Room A?

2. The area of Room B is $(30x + 12y - 12)$ square units. What are possible dimensions of Room B?

3. If Room B has the dimensions you found in Exercise 2, what is its perimeter? Show how you found your answer.

4. A partition can be used to divide Room C into two smaller rectangular rooms as shown in the diagram below. The width of room C is greater than 1 unit. Complete the diagram by filling in the width of Room C and the lengths of the two smaller rooms.

[ ] units   [ ] units

[ ] units
| Area: $(21x - 7)$ square units | Area: $(14x + 35y)$ square units |

5. The total area of Room C is $(35x + 35y - 7)$ square units. Factor this expression and explain how the factors are related to your answers to Exercise 4.

Name _____

Raul and Bobby are brothers who are saving to buy a new video game console. Bobby contributed $25 and plans to save $10 per week. Raul contributed $20 and plans to save $15 per week. What expression represents the total amount Bobby and Raul will have in w weeks?

$25 + 10w$	Write an expression for Bobby's savings.
$20 + 15w$	Write an expression for Raul's savings.
$(25 + 10w) + (20 + 15w)$	Add the expressions.
$(25 + 20) + (10w + 15w)$	Use the Commutative and Associative Properties.
$45 + 25w$	Combine like terms.

The expression $45 + 25w$ represents the total amount they will have in w weeks.

For membership to a bulk grocery store, there is a $55 initial fee and monthly dues are $12.50. A gym membership costs $69.95 a month, plus a one-time sign up fee of $90. What expression represents the total cost of both memberships for m months?

1. Complete the diagram.

2. What expression represents the total monthly cost of the bulk grocery store membership?

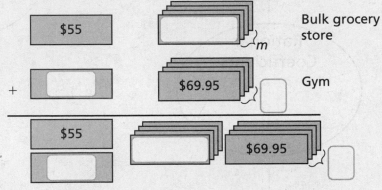

3. What expression represents the total monthly cost of the gym membership?

4. Write the sum of the expressions from Exercises 2 and 3.

5. Use the Commutative and Associative Properties to rewrite your expression with like terms grouped together. Then combine like terms to write an expression that represents the total cost of both memberships for m months.

On the Back!

6. For adults, a bowling alley charges $3.75 for shoe rental and $5 per game. For children, the cost is $2.50 for shoe rental and $4 per game. What expression represents the total cost for one adult and one child to bowl g games?

Each oval section of the graphic organizer contains two examples.
Use the list below to complete the graphic organizer. Place each term
in the most specific section possible.

$1.11b$	-7	$-3n$	$\frac{2}{3}$	y	$-\frac{5}{2}x$

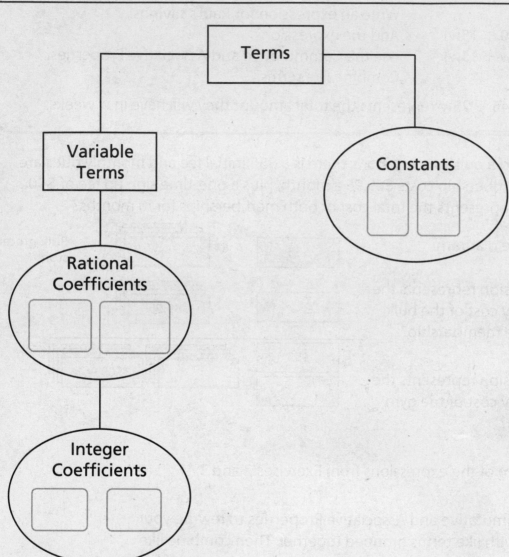

Name _____

**Read the word problem below. Then answer the questions to
help you understand the problem.**

An online bookstore sells all paperback books for x dollars each. Aidan
bought 7 paperback books and spent $3.95 on shipping. Nina bought
11 paperback books and spent $5.25 on shipping. What expression
represents the total amount that Aidan and Nina spent?

1. Underline the question that you need to answer.

2. What does it mean when a problem asks for an expression?

3. Circle the part of the problem that represents the cost of a book.

4. How can you find the cost of Nina's books?

   ☐ The problem states that Nina's books cost $11.

   ☐ Add 11 and x.

   ☐ Multiply 11 and x.

   ☐ Add 11 and 5.25.

5. After simplifying, how many terms do you expect in your final
   answer? Explain.

Name _____

Tia, Will, and Ana each have some pennies, nickels, and dimes. The table below provides information about the number of coins each person has.

	Tia	Will	Ana
Pennies	x	2 times as many as Tia	5 fewer than Will
Nickels	1 more than 3 times as many as Will	y	7
Dimes	2 fewer than Ana	3 times as many as Ana	z

1. Write expressions to represent the total number of coins that each person has. Then simplify each expression.

2. Add the expressions to find the total number of coins for all three people combined.

3. Write expressions to represent the total value in cents of each person's coins. Then simplify each expression. Can you use the simplified expressions you wrote for Exercise 1 to help you? Explain.

4. Add the expressions to find the total value of the coins for all three people combined.

A meal delivery service called Healthy Foods charges an initial fee of $29.95 plus $25 each month. Good Eats provides the same service for an initial fee of $10 plus $20 a month. Write an expression that represents the amount Miranda will save over m months if she signs up for Good Eats instead of Healthy Foods.

$(29.95 + 25m) - (10 + 20m)$ Subtract expressions for the cost of each membership.

$= 29.95 + 25m - 10 - 20m$ Distributive Property

$= (25m - 20m) + (29.95 - 10)$ Commutative and Associative Properties

$= 5m + 19.95$ Combine like terms.

Miranda will save $5m + 19.95$ dollars if she signs up for Good Eats instead of Healthy Foods.

Last week, Byron bought 5 containers of yogurt and spent $12.88 on other groceries. This week Cassandra bought 3 containers of the same yogurt and spent $11.50 on other groceries. How much more money did Byron spend than Cassandra?

1. Let c represent the cost of one container of yogurt. Write expressions to represent the amount spent by Byron and the amount spent by Cassandra.

2. Write an expression to represent the difference by subtracting the amount that Cassandra spent from the amount that Byron spent. Then complete the steps to simplify the expression.

$\left(\boxed{} \right) - \left(\boxed{} \right)$

$= 5c + 12.88 - \boxed{} - \boxed{}$

$= \left(5c - \boxed{} \right) + \left(\boxed{} - 11.50 \right)$

$= \boxed{} c + \boxed{}$

3. What expression represents how much more money Byron spent than Cassandra?

On the Back!

4. Yesterday Gunnar ran 4 times around the track plus an additional 450 feet. Today he ran 3 times around the track plus an additional 375 feet. What expression represents how much farther Gunnar ran yesterday than today?

Name _____

Use the list below to complete the sentences.

Commutative Property	**parentheses**	**distribute**	**signs**
like terms	**terms**	**Associative Property**	

Subtract and simplify $(5x + 3y) - (6x + 2y - 1)$.

1. When you subtract one expression from another expression,
   you can _____ the minus sign to all the
   _____ in the second expression.

   $(5x + 3y) - (6x + 2y - 1) = 5x + 3y + (-1)(6x) + (-1)(2y) + (-1)(-1)$

2. When each term in the second expression is multiplied by -1, the
   _____ of the terms in the second expression are
   changed.

   $5x + 3y + (-1)(6x) + (-1)(2y) + (-1)(-1) = 5x + 3y - 6x - 2y + 1$

3. The original problem is now written without any
   _____.

4. Next, reorder the terms using the _____
   so that like terms are together.

   $5x + 3y - 6x - 2y + 1 = 5x - 6x + 3y - 2y + 1$

5. Finally, use the _____ to regroup
   and combine _____.

   $5x - 6x + 3y - 2y + 1 = (5x - 6x) + (3y - 2y) + 1 = -x + y + 1$

Name _____

**Read the problem below. Answer the questions to
help understand the steps needed to solve the problem.**

Chantelle and Henry work for the same company and share a reception
area and a conference room as shown below. How much greater is the
area of Chantelle's office than the area of Henry's office?

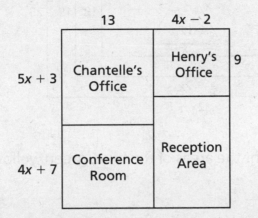

1. How many operations will you use to answer the question? Name
   each operation and underline the word or words in the problem
   that tell you this.

2. In the diagram, highlight the given side lengths of the two offices
   that you need to compare. Cross out any information in the
   problem and diagram that is not necessary to solve the problem.

3. Complete the table to organize the information you will need to
   solve the problem.

	Chantelle's Office	Henry's Office
Length	13 units	[ ] units
Width	[ ] units	9 units
Area	13 ([ ]) square units	9 ([ ]) square units

4. Once you have found the areas of Chantelle's and Henry's offices,
   will you have completed the problem? Explain.

Billy and Derek are designing a flag for their treehouse fort.
The diagram below shows the design of their flag.

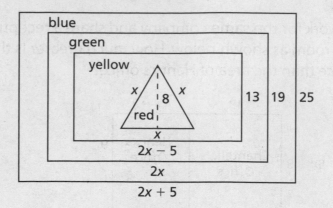

1. Write expressions to represent the areas of the blue, green, yellow,
   and red sections.

2. Add the areas of each section to find the total area of the flag.
   Explain how you can check this solution.

3. A white border will be placed around the edges of each section.
   Write and simplify an expression to find the total lengths of all the
   white borders.

Name _____

The price of a pair of jeans has been reduced by 40%. Let p represent the original price.

The equivalent expressions $p - 0.4p$ and $0.6p$ represent the sale price of the jeans.

The expression $p - 0.4p$ means that 40% was subtracted from the original price, p.

p

| $p - 0.4p$, or $0.6p$ | $0.4p$ |

The expression $0.6p$ means that 40% off the original price, p, is equivalent to 60% of the original price.

Antoine is moving to a new house. His new room will be 50% larger than his old room. What equivalent expressions can you use to represent the size of Antoine's new room?

1. Let r represent the size of Antoine's old room. What expression represents how much larger his new room is than his old room?

2. Draw a bar diagram to represent Antoine's new room.

3. What addition expression represents the size of Antoine's new room? How can you write an equivalent expression?

On the Back!

4. For her summer vacation, Emily reduced the weight of her luggage by 30% from its weight, s, on her winter vacation. Write two equivalent expressions to represent the weight of Emily's luggage on her summer vacation.

Use the list below to fill in an example for each property or technique.

$5 + x = x + 5$	$3x + 6 = 3(x + 2)$	$x - 4 = x + (-4)$
$3a + 2 + a = 4a + 2$	$(2x + 7) + 3 = 2x + (7 + 3)$	

Property or Technique	Example
Distributive Property	
Associative Property	
Commutative Property	
Combine like terms.	
Write an additive inverse.	

For each of the following, tell whether the expressions are *equivalent expressions* or *not equivalent expressions*.

1. $16b + 7a - c$ and $7a + (-c) + 16b$

   equivalent expressions   not equivalent expressions

2. $5y + (-4)$ and $4 + (-5y)$

   equivalent expressions   not equivalent expressions

3. $x + x + 3 - y + 2x - 1 + 6y$ and $4x + 5y + 2$

   equivalent expressions   not equivalent expressions

Name _____

**Read the problem below. Answer the questions to help
you understand the steps for solving the problem.**

Mr. Kelley uses an expression to represent the perimeter of a square.
How can the expression be rewritten to highlight the length of a side
of the square?

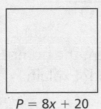

$P = 8x + 20$

1. Underline the expression representing the perimeter of the square.
   Circle the words in the problem that explain what this expression
   represents.

2. Which of the following best describes the correct solution to this
   problem?

   ☐ An explanation written in words

   ☐ An algebraic expression that represents the perimeter of the square

   ☐ An algebraic expression that represents the side length of the square

   ☐ The actual side length of the square given as a number

3. How can you rewrite an expression with no like terms?

4. What is the relationship between the perimeter of a square and its
   side length? Select all correct answers.

   ☐ Perimeter = (side length) + (side length) + (side length) + (side length)

   ☐ Perimeter = (side length) × (side length)

   ☐ Perimeter = 4 × (side length)

   ☐ Perimeter = (side length) ÷ 4

Name _____

A conference center has rectangular tables that seat three people at each long side and one person at each end. Tables can be placed end-to-end to seat larger groups, as shown in the diagram.

1. Why does the expression $6x + 2$ represent the number of people who can sit at x tables placed end-to-end? Explain.

2. An individual table can seat 8 people, but people cannot sit at the ends of the middle tables or the inside ends of the end tables when the tables are placed end to end. An event planner thinks the expression $8x - 2(x - 2) - 2(1)$ can also be used to represent the number of people that can be seated. Is the event planner's expression equivalent to $6x + 2$? Show your work.

3. Write another expression that is equivalent to $6x + 2$. How does your expression represent the number of people who can sit at x tables placed end-to-end?

4. If the tables were placed side-by-side so that the long sides were next to each other instead of the short sides, what expression represents the number of people who can sit at x tables? Explain.

Name _____

Solve Problems Using Equations and Inequalities

Dear Family,

   Your child is learning to write and solve equations and inequalities that represent real-world situations. He or she is using models to represent these situations and to help translate these situations into mathematical sentences. Your child is also learning to graph solutions of inequalities on number lines.

   Here is an activity you can do with your child to help him or her practice solving and graphing inequalities.

Solve and Graph Inequalities

Materials: number cube

Step 1 Roll a number cube three times. Write a one-digit number and a two-digit number using the digits you rolled.

Step 2 Write an inequality using the two numbers, a variable, and one of the inequality symbols $<$, $>$, $\leq$, or $\geq$. For example, if you roll the numbers 4, 6, and 1, you might write $x + 4 \leq 61$.

Step 3 Ask your child to solve the inequality and graph the solution.

Observe Your Child

Focus on Mathematical Practices

Construct viable arguments and critique the reasoning of others.

Help your child become proficient with this Mathematical Practice. Have your child connect the graph to the inequality. Select a number that is not included in the graph, and ask your child to explain why this number is not a solution to the original inequality. Then select a number that is included in the graph, and ask your child to explain why this number is a solution.

Nombre _____

Resolver problemas usando ecuaciones y desigualdades

Estimada familia:

Su hijo o hija está aprendiendo a escribir y resolver ecuaciones y desigualdades que representan situaciones de la vida diaria. Usará modelos para representar esas situaciones y para traducirlas a oraciones matemáticas. También está aprendiendo a graficar soluciones de desigualdades en rectas numéricas.

Esta es una actividad que puede realizar con su hijo o hija para que practique cómo resolver y graficar desigualdades.

Resolver y graficar desigualdades

Materiales: Cubo numérico

Paso 1 Lancen un cubo numérico tres veces. Con los números que obtuvieron, escriban un número de un dígito y un número de dos dígitos.

Paso 2 Escriban una desigualdad con los dos números, una variable y uno de los símbolos de desigualdad ($<$, $>$, $\leq$ o $\geq$). Por ejemplo, si obtuvieron los números 4, 6 y 1 al lanzar el cubo numérico, pueden escribir $x + 4 \leq 61$.

Paso 3 Pida a su hijo o hija que resuelva la desigualdad y que grafique la solución.

Observe a su hijo o hija

Enfoque en las Prácticas matemáticas
Construir argumentos viables y evaluar el razonamiento de otros.

Ayude a su hijo o hija a adquirir competencia en esta Práctica matemática. Pídale que relacione la gráfica con la desigualdad. Escoja un número que no esté incluido en la gráfica y pida a su hijo o hija que explique por qué ese número no es la solución de la desigualdad original. Luego, escoja un número que esté incluido en la gráfica y pídale que explique por qué ese número es la solución.

Name _____

Venn Diagrams

How would you sort a basket of vegetables? A pile of toys?

A Venn diagram shows the relationships among a specified number of sets. Each region describes one of the sets. Regions that overlap show characteristics shared by the sets. Some Venn diagrams have regions that are completely inside another region, and some have regions that are completely separate.

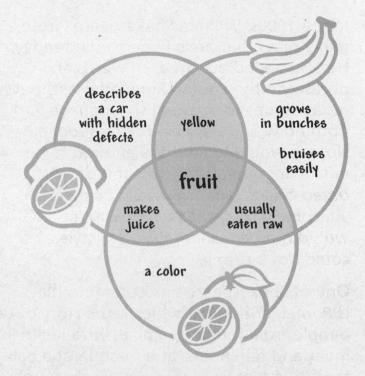

Your Project **Comparing With a Venn Diagram**

Make at least one Venn diagram to show your understanding of equations and inequalities. Use the vocabulary words from the topic as well as other descriptives. What things are unique to equations? What things are unique to inequalities? What will you include in the overlapping section or sections of your Venn diagram? Make a poster of your Venn diagram.

Name _____

Feuding Families

In the 1600s, William Shakespeare wrote many plays that are still performed today. He also added hundreds of words and phrases to the English language. Without his additions to the English language, nothing would happen *all of a sudden*. No one would laugh hard enough to be *in stitches* or wait for something *with bated breath*. No one would be able to welcome a *tranquil dawn*. Clothing would not be *fashionable*, and style could not be *zany*.

One of Shakespeare's most famous plays is *Romeo and Juliet*, which is the story of two people from feuding families who fall in love. Romeo and Juliet meet and fall in love at a masquerade ball. The feud between their two families keeps the young couple apart and ultimately leads to tragedy.

• •

Your Project **Write a Play**

Write a play about two feuding families: the Equations and the Inequalities. Your play must include a love story between an Equation and an Inequality. Why do they fall in love? How do they reconcile the differences between their families and themselves? What is the final outcome?

Use what you have learned about in this topic to help you develop your play. Submit your final script to your teacher.

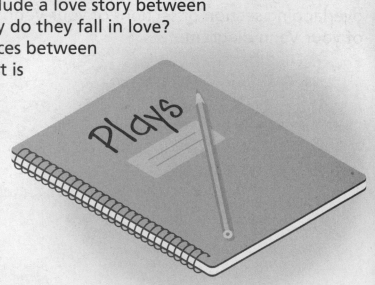

Name _____

Foreign Exchange Program

A foreign exchange program gives students an opportunity to attend school in another country. For a few weeks to a few months, a student lives with a host family, attends a local school, and explores the country's culture. Students usually have to learn a new language, become familiar with new cultural norms, and adjust to other differences from their home country.

· ·

Your Project **Exchange Souvenirs**

If you were visiting another country, think about what you might bring from home to show and explain your culture.

Suppose two countries on the planet Analogia are Equali, a land of equations, and Inequali, a land of inequalities. The two countries have a foreign exchange program every year. Each exchange student must keep a journal describing his or her experiences. They also are encouraged to bring back at least three souvenirs to teach classmates at home about the host country.

Work with a partner. One of you should make at least three items that an exchange student might bring home as souvenirs, and write at least two journal entries from the perspective of an exchange student from Equali. The other should do the same as an exchange student from Inequali. The journal entries should compare the two countries through your imagined experiences and should describe the importance of each souvenir. Highlight the similarities and differences between your home country and your host country. The journal entries should cover the concepts you have learned in this topic.

Name _____

Be Prepared for Anything

Many people like game shows. Some people plan a vacation to participate in a game show studio audience. Others enter competitions or take tests to become contestants on a game show. Being on a game show often requires having a wide range of knowledge, staying calm under pressure, and being prepared for anything.

Your Project **Solve Randomized Equations and Inequalities**

Suppose you are auditioning for a game show. For the audition, you have to be prepared to solve equations and inequalities. Draw three nets for cubes. On the first net, write each operation (=, <, and >) on two faces. On the second net, write an integer on each face, including at least one negative integer. On the third net, write a multi-step expression on each face. At least one expression should require using the Distributive Property to simplify. Assemble your cubes.

Roll your cubes 10 times and prepare a solution sheet for the 10 equations or inequalities.

For your game show audition, give your teacher your cubes and your solution sheet. Your teacher will roll the cubes, and you must solve whichever equation or inequality comes up. Remember: Be prepared for anything!

Name _____

Water Is Life!

Water Access

Research and consider some types of water filters used in developing countries.

Filtration System	Approximate Cost ($)	Water Capacity	Pros (+) and Cons (−)

Water Is Life!

Water Access, *continued*

Why	Why is it important to filter water before using it? What are the risks of using unfiltered or untreated water?
What	What should you use filtered water for?
Amount	How much water does each person need to survive?
Choose	If you want to provide water to a village of 175 people, which filtration system(s) would you choose? Why?
Buying	Write and solve an equation to determine the cost of purchasing the water filtration system(s) for the village.

Name _____

Water Is Life!

Fundraising

Research and consider various methods of fundraising.

Fundraiser Type	Approximate Fundraising Potential ($)	Pros (+) and Cons (–)

Water Is Life!
Fundraising, *continued*

Amount	What amount of money would you need to fundraise to provide your chosen water filtration system to the community? Use the information from your Water Access worksheet.
Choose	Based on the information above, which type of fundraiser would you choose? Explain.
Calculate	Write an equation that you can use to determine how much money you raise from your fundraiser. Solve the equation for the amount of money you need to raise to consider your fundraiser a success.

Henry's suitcase weighs 55 pounds. This is 7 pounds more than 3 times the weight of Matthew's suitcase. What equation can be used to relate the weights of Henry's and Matthew's suitcases?

The equation $55 = 3m + 7$ can be used to relate the weights of Henry's and Matthew's suitcases.

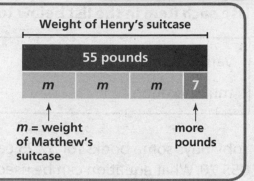

Weight of Henry's suitcase

55 pounds

| m | m | m | 7 |

m = weight of Matthew's suitcase

more pounds

Rosalyn has 185 contacts in her phone. That is 5 more than twice the number of contacts Laila has in her phone. What equation represents the relationship between the numbers of contacts Rosalyn and Laila have in their phones?

1. Complete the bar diagram.

Number of Contacts in Rosalyn's Phone

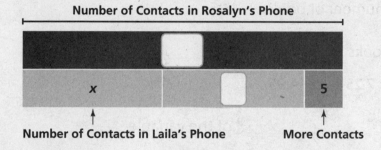

| x | | | 5 |

Number of Contacts in Laila's Phone   More Contacts

2. What does the variable x represent?

3. What expression represents the number of contacts in Rosalyn's phone in terms of the contacts in Laila's phone?

4. What equation can be used to represent the relationship between the numbers of contacts Rosalyn and Laila have in their phones?

On the Back!

5. Josh has $252 in his bank account. This is $12 more than 6 times the amount of money that Sally has in her bank account. What equation can be used to represent the relationship between the amounts of money Josh and Sally have in their bank accounts?

Name _____

Use each item in the list below to complete each sentence.

| variable | constant | substitute |
| multiplication | coefficient | addition |

Toby buys some books for $7.25 each and a magazine for $4.95. His total bill before tax is $55.70. What equation can be used to represent the situation?

Toby writes the following equation to model the situation.

total cost = cost of each book · number of books + cost of the magazine

1. Next, _____ the given values into the equation;

$$55.70 = 7.25 \cdot \text{number of books} + 4.95$$

2. To represent the number of books Toby buys, use a(n) _____ ;

$$55.70 = 7.25 \cdot b + 4.95$$

3. In this equation, 7.25 is the _____ of the variable
   and 4.95 is the _____ .

4. To find the cost of the books, this equation uses _____ .
   To combine all the costs, this equation uses _____ .

Indicate whether each equation below is a *one-step equation* or a *two-step equation*.

5. $25 = x + 3$

   one-step equation   two-step equation

6. $2b - 7 = 15$

   one-step equation   two-step equation

7. $10m = 90$

   one-step equation   two-step equation

Name ______________________________

Build Mathematical Literacy
6-1

Read the word problem below. Then answer the questions to understand the problem.

Natalie uses 68 photos to make an online photo album. She can fit 5 photos on each page. She fills all of the pages in her album except for the last page, which has 2 empty spaces. What equation can be used to find the number of pages in the album?

1. Underline the key information in the problem.

2. Is the answer to this problem a number? Explain.

3. Circle the quantity that will be represented by a variable. Explain how you determined this from the problem.

The total number of photos

The number of photos per page

The number of pages in the album

The number of empty spaces

4. What is the total number of photos the album can hold if the album has *p* pages? Explain.

5. Which expression represents the number of photos in the album, $5p + 2$ or $5p - 2$? Explain your choice.

Name _____

The table below shows the values of currencies in U.S. dollars on the day that the students exchanged their money.

Currency	Value in U.S. Dollars
1 Canadian Dollar	0.7386
1 British Pound	1.5395
1 Euro	1.0982
1 Japanese Yen	0.0093
1 Brazilian Real	0.2547

1. Vivian exchanged her Japanese yen for $56.92 in U.S. dollars. What equation can be used to find the quantity of Japanese yen that Vivian exchanged?

2. Xavier had $28.00 in U.S. dollars as well as some British pounds. After exchanging his British pounds for U.S. dollars, Xavier had a total of $92.15. What equation can be used to find the quantity of British pounds that Xavier exchanged?

3. Tobias exchanged his Canadian dollars for U.S. dollars and then gave $15.75 to Margaret. After giving money to Margaret, he had $41.87 remaining. What equation can be used to find the quantity of Canadian dollars that Tobias exchanged?

4. Gwen had 5 euros and some Brazilian reals. After exchanging all of her money for U.S. dollars, she had $81.62. What equation can be used to find the quantity of Brazilian reals that Gwen exchanged?

5. Kayla had some euros. Jin had the same number of Canadian dollars. After both girls exchanged their money for U.S. dollars, Kayla had $8.63 more than Jin. What equation can be used to find the quantity of euros that Kayla exchanged?

Name _____

Ted bought 2 bags of gravel and a potted tree that weighed 7.4 pounds at Marvin's Garden Shoppe. The total weight of his purchases was 16 pounds. How much did each bag of gravel weigh?

Use a bar diagram and an equation to represent the situation. Then solve the equation.

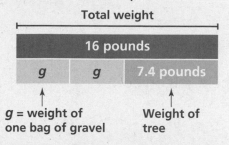

Total weight

$$2g + 7.4 = 16$$
$$2g + 7.4 - 7.4 = 16 - 7.4$$
$$2g = 8.6$$
$$\frac{2g}{2} = \frac{8.6}{2}$$
$$g = 4.3$$

Each bag of gravel weighed 4.3 pounds.

Three friends ate lunch at a restaurant. Their friend Reggie arrived late and only ordered a glass of juice. The total bill was $39.50 before taxes. Reggie paid $2 for his juice, and the others divided the remaining amount equally. How much did each of Reggie's three friends pay?

1. Complete the bar diagram.

2. Fill in the boxes to write and solve an equation.

$$\boxed{}x + \boxed{} = 39.50$$
$$3x + 2 - \boxed{} = 39.50 - \boxed{}$$
$$3x = \boxed{}$$
$$\frac{3x}{\boxed{}} = \frac{\boxed{}}{\boxed{}}$$
$$x = \boxed{}$$

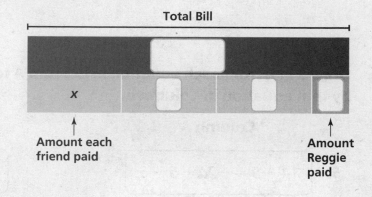

Total Bill

Amount each friend paid

Amount Reggie paid

3. How much did each of Reggie's three friends pay?

On the Back!

4. Blair's new computer cost $5 less than twice the cost of her old computer. Her new computer cost $709. How much did Blair's old computer cost?

Name _____

Use each item from the list below once to complete each sentence.

inverse	properties of equality
variable	bar diagram

1. One way to represent an equation is to use a(n) _____.

2. When solving an equation, you perform the same operation on both sides of the equation using the _____.

3. To "undo" operations in an equation, use the _____ operation.

4. The final step in solving a two-step equation is to isolate the _____.

Draw a line from each equation in Column A to the name of the property illustrated by that equation in Column B.

Column A

5. $14 - 5 = -2a + 5 - 5$

6. $\dfrac{-13y}{-13} = \dfrac{52}{-13}$

7. $9x - 7 + 7 = 52 + 7$

Column B

Addition Property of Equality

Subtraction Property of Equality

Division Property of Equality

Name ______________________________

Build Mathematical Literacy
6-2

Read the word problem below. Then answer the questions to identify the steps for solving the problem.

Ana baked 82 muffins for her school's bake sale. She put 4 muffins aside for her friends and placed the remaining muffins on plates to sell. Ana placed 6 muffins on each plate. How many plates did she use?

1. Underline the question that you need to answer.

2. Circle the quantities that you can use to write an equation that represents the situation.

3. Which of the following equations represents the situation? What does the variable *p* represent?

- ☐ $4p + 6 = 82$
- ☐ $6p + 4 = 82$
- ☐ $6(p + 4) = 82$
- ☐ $6p - 4 = 82$

4. How can you use the equation to find the answer?

5. What type of number must the answer to this problem be? Explain.

The snowy tree cricket is sometimes called the temperature cricket because the frequency of its chirps varies based on the temperature. The number of snowy tree cricket chirps per minute is 148 less than 4 times the outside temperature in degrees Fahrenheit.

1. Write an equation that relates the number of chirps per minute, x, and the outside temperature in degrees Fahrenheit, f. What is the outside temperature if a snowy tree cricket chirps 100 times in a minute?

2. How much greater is the temperature in degrees Fahrenheit when the snowy tree cricket chirps 140 times per minute than when it chirps 120 times per minute?

3. What is the change in chirps per minute for each increase in temperature by 1 degree Fahrenheit? Explain your answer.

4. When you multiply a temperature in degrees Celsius by $\frac{9}{5}$ and then add 32, the result is the equivalent temperature in degrees Fahrenheit. Write an equation that you can use to find the temperature in degrees Celsius, c, when you know the temperature in degrees Fahrenheit, f. What is the temperature in degrees Fahrenheit and in degrees Celsius when the snowy tree cricket chirps 160 times per minute?

Name _____

Four friends each bought a ticket to a concert. In addition to the ticket price, each friend paid a service fee of $5.50 to the ticket broker. The four friends paid a total of $126. What was the price of each ticket?

Let t represent the price of a ticket.
Then the expression $t + 5.50$ represents
the amount paid by each person.

$$4(t + 5.50) = 126$$
$$4t + 22 = 126$$
$$4t + 22 - 22 = 126 - 22$$
$$4t = 104$$
$$\frac{4t}{4} = \frac{104}{4}$$

The price of each ticket was $26.
$$t = 26$$

A class of 24 students visited a science museum. Each student paid the museum's admission fee and $6 for lunch at the museum. The class spent a total of $336. What was the admission fee that each student paid?

1. Let f represent the museum's admission fee. What expression represents the total amount paid by each student?

2. Use the expression from Exercise 1 to write an expression that represents the total amount paid by the entire class.

3. Use the expression from Exercise 2 to write an equation that represents the situation.

4. Rewrite the equation using the Distributive Property.

5. Solve the equation. What was the admission fee that each student paid?

On the Back!

6. A grocer bought 25 bags of flour from a wholesaler. He marked up the price of each bag by $1.50, sold all of the flour for a total of $87.50. How much did the grocer pay the wholesaler for each bag of flour?

se each term from the list below once to complete each sentence.

multiplying	properties of equality	Distributive Property
expanded form	solution	area model

1. For the equation $5(x + 1) = 20$, $x = 3$ is the

   _____.

2. To solve the equation $2(x - 1) = 8$, you use the

   _____ to rewrite $2(x - 1)$ as $2x - 2$.

3. To apply the Distributive Property to the expression $5(a + 3)$,

   distribute the 5 by _____ each term

   inside the parentheses by 5.

4. The expression $4b + 8$ is the _____ of $4(b + 2)$.

5. To solve the equation, $-6(x + 2) = 30$, you can distribute the

   negative number and then use the _____.

6. To represent a situation that involves the Distributive Property, you

   can often use a(n) _____.

Name _____

Read the word problem below. Then answer the questions to understand the problem.

Five friends went to a movie. Each friend bought a ticket and a medium-sized bag of popcorn. The total amount they spent was $61.25. What was the price of each movie ticket?

Popcorn Prices	
Size	**Price**
Small	$2.25
Medium	$3.75
Large	$5.50

1. Underline the question that you need to answer.

2. What will be the unit of the answer?

3. Circle the information you can use to write an equation that represents the situation.

4. What must be true about the price of each movie ticket in order to solve the problem with the given information?

5. Explain which given information is not needed to solve the problem.

Name _____

Read the clues below about the current ages of some of the members of the Ruiz family.

Person	Age
Juan	4 less than twice Maria's age
Amara	3 times Juan's age
Carlos	4 more than Tony's age
Lilly	One more than 6 times Tony's age
Sofia	2 times the combined ages of Carlos and Lilly
Ben	Half the combined ages of Maria, Tony, and Isabelle

1. Write an equation that relates Juan's age, j, to Maria's age, m.

2. Amara is 18 years old. Use the equation from Exercise 1 to write an equation that relates Amara's age and Maria's age. How old is Maria?

3. Sofia is 38 years old. Write an equation that relates Sofia's age to Tony's age, t. How old is Tony?

4. Ben is one year younger than Amara. Write an equation that can be used to find Isabelle's age, I. How old is Isabelle?

5. Will the equation $a = 3(2m - 4)$ represent the relationship between Amara's age, a, and Maria's age, m, when they are each one year older? Support your answer.

Name _____

Each day, Maura is allowed to play video games for no more than 60 minutes. She has already played for 28 minutes today. For how many more minutes can Maura play video games today?

Let m represent the number of minutes Maura can still play today.

Write and solve an inequality.

$$28 + m \leq 60$$
$$28 - 28 + m \leq 60 - 28$$
$$m \leq 32$$

Use a number line to show all of the possible solutions.

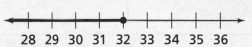

28 29 30 31 32 33 34 35 36

Maura may play video games for no more than 32 additional minutes today.

Vin has saved $62 so far this month. His goal is to save at least $100 by the end of the month. How much can Vin save from now until the end of the month to reach his goal?

1. Let s represent the amount Vin saves from now until the end of the month. Write an expression that represents Vin's total savings this month.

2. Write an inequality that shows that Vin's total savings for the month are at least $100.

3. Solve the inequality from Exercise 2 and show all of the possible solutions on the number line.

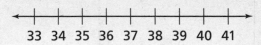

33 34 35 36 37 38 39 40 41

4. How much can Vin save from now until the end of the month to meet his goal?

On the Back!

5. Three students have already enrolled for a creative writing class. The teacher will cancel the class if there are fewer than 10 students enrolled. Write three values for numbers of students needed to sign up so that the the creative writing class can be held.

Complete the vocabulary chart.

Word or Phrase	Definition	Picture or Example
greater than		$109 > 47$ $y > 3$
at most	At most is a comparison of two values in which the first value is located in the same location as, or to the left of, the second value on a number line.	
less than	Less than is a comparison of two values in which the first value is located to the left of the second value on a number line.	
at least		$55 \geq 45$ $a \geq 18$
cannot exceed		$x \leq 10$ $8 \leq 9$

Name _____

**Read the word problem. Then answer the questions to
understand the problem.**

Don earned $75 fixing computers. He used $17 to buy a book. Next,
he wants to buy some clothes. Write an inequality to show how much
money Don can spend on clothes.

1. Underline the sentence that tells you what you need to do to solve
    this problem.

2. Does the problem ask for a specific amount that Don can spend on
    clothes? Explain.

3. Which of the following best represents the situation? Explain.

    ☐   cost of book + cost of clothes ≥ total amount earned

    ☐   cost of book + cost of clothes < total amount earned

    ☐   cost of book + cost of clothes ≤ total amount earned

4. Complete the table with information given in the problem. Use the
    variable *x* to represent unknown information.

Cost of Book	
Cost of Clothes	
Total Amount Earned	

Name _____

The following table shows the number of students currently registered for some classes offered next semester. Enrollment requirements for each class are also shown.

Class	Students Registered	Enrollment Requirement	Additional Students
Advanced French	12	no more than 15	
Concert Band	42	at least 56	
Woodworking	11	fewer than 20	
Ceramics	6	more than 12	

1. Write inequalities to show the number of additional students who may register for each class. Write the solution of the inequality representing each class in the last column in the table.

2. Suppose enough additional students register for woodworking and ceramics to meet the enrollment requirements. If the number of additional woodworking students is one more than the number of additional ceramics students, how many students will be in each class? Explain.

3. The economics class can have no more than 22 students, but the teacher allows more than 22 students to register because she expects 6 students to cancel their enrollments. Write and solve an inequality to describe the number of students that could register for the economics class. Explain.

Benny has $450 in his bank account. For how many weeks can Benny withdraw $50 per week from this account?

Let w represent the number of weeks.
Write and solve an inequality.

$$50w \leq 450$$
$$\frac{50w}{50} \leq \frac{450}{50}$$
$$w \leq 9$$

Use a number line to show all of the possible solutions.

4   5   6   7   8   9   10   11   12

Benny can withdraw $50 per week for up to 9 weeks.

Manuel has been training for a bike race. He now rides 35 miles during each training session. This is more than 5 times the distance he rode during each session when he first began training. What are the possible distances Manuel rode during each session when he began training?

1. Let d represent the distance Manuel rode during each session when he began training. Write an expression that represents 5 times this distance.

2. Use the expression from Exercise 1 to write an inequality that relates the distance Manuel now rides to the distance he rode when he began training.

3. Solve the inequality from Exercise 2 and graph the solution on the number line.

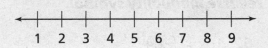

1   2   3   4   5   6   7   8   9

4. What are the possible distances Manuel rode during each session when he began training?

On the Back!

5. Shari has 7 months to save $294 for a vacation. How much must Shari save each month in order to save at least $294 for her vacation?

Use each item from the list below to complete each sentence.

coefficient	Multiplication Property of Inequality	reciprocal
reverse	Division Property of Inequality	negative

1. The _____ of $\frac{5}{7}$ is $\frac{7}{5}$.

2. When you multiply or divide both sides of an inequality
   by the same _____ number, you
   _____ the inequality symbol.

3. When you divide both sides of $3x > 12$ by 3 to isolate x, you are
   using the _____ to solve
   the inequality.

4. In the inequality $9b > 45$, 9 is the _____
   of the variable b.

5. To solve the inequality $\frac{n}{4} \geq 2$, use the _____
   _____ to multiply both sides by 4.

**For each inequality, highlight the number you use to determine whether you need
to reverse the inequality symbol. Then circle _reverse inequality symbol_ or _do not
reverse inequality symbol_.**

6. $16x > -64$

   reverse inequality symbol   do not reverse inequality symbol

7. $-\frac{2}{9}x < 3$

   reverse inequality symbol   do not reverse inequality symbol

8. $-15 \geq -5b$

   reverse inequality symbol   do not reverse inequality symbol

Review the Key Concept box from the lesson.
Then answer the questions to help you understand
how to read a Key Concept.

KEY CONCEPT

Solving inequalities with multiplication and division is the same as solving
equations with multiplication and division when the values are positive. Use the
inverse relationship between multiplication and division to isolate the variable.

$2.5x \geq 15$

$\dfrac{2.5x}{2.5} \geq \dfrac{15}{2.5}$ Use inverse relationships and properties
of inequality to isolate the variable.

$x \geq 6$

When multiplying or dividing by negative values, the inequality symbol is reversed.

$-2.5x \geq 15$

$\dfrac{-2.5x}{-2.5} \leq \dfrac{15}{-2.5}$ Dividing by a negative value
reverses the inequality.

$x \leq -6$

1. Underline the words in the first paragraph of the Key Concept box
    that describe what to do when multiplying or dividing both sides of
    an inequality by a positive value.

2. Look at the example under the first paragraph. What operation is
    performed on both sides of the inequality? How does this example
    illustrate the first paragraph?

3. What does it mean to reverse an inequality symbol?

Name _____

The prices of some items at a snack stand are shown in the table.

Item	Price ($)
Yogurt	1.85
Juice	1.15
Soft Pretzel	2.05
Granola Bar	1.30

1. Olivia bought some granola bars and spent at least $6.24. Write and solve an inequality to find the number of granola bars she bought. Explain the real-world meaning of the solution.

2. Write and solve an inequality to find the possible numbers of bottles of juice you could buy with $9.89. Explain the real-world meaning of the solution.

3. Jada spent less than $7.79 to buy some soft pretzels. Can the inequality $-2.05x > -7.79$ be used to find the number of pretzels she could buy? If so, explain why, solve the inequality, and explain the real-world meaning of your solution. If not, explain why not, and write and solve a correct inequality, and explain the real-world meaning of the solution.

4. Lamar has x younger siblings. He bought a container of yogurt and a granola bar for each of them and spent less than $15.12. Write and solve an inequality to find the number of younger siblings Lamar could have. Explain the real-world meaning of the solution.

Ryan can spend no more than $6 at an office supply store. He needs to buy some paste that costs $2.58 and make several copies of a flyer. If copies cost $0.18 each, how many copies, c, can Ryan make?

Write an inequality to represent the situation.

$$\frac{\text{Cost of}}{\text{paste}} + \frac{\text{Cost of}}{\text{one copy}} \cdot \frac{\text{Number}}{\text{of copies}} \leq \frac{\text{Money}}{\text{available}}$$

$$2.58 + 0.18c \leq 6$$
$$2.58 - 2.58 + 0.18c \leq 6 - 2.58$$
$$0.18c \leq 3.42$$
$$\frac{0.18c}{0.18} \leq \frac{3.42}{0.18}$$
$$c \leq 19$$

Ryan can make 19 or fewer copies.

Alice is planning her next vacation. She budgeted $110 for travel expenses, and she expects to spend $120 each day for food and lodging. Her total budget for the trip is $710. How many days, d, can Alice have for her vacation without exceeding her budget?

1. Complete the inequality.

[   ] + [   ] · [   ]

Number of days $\leq$ [   ]

2. Fill in the boxes to write and solve the inequality.

$$110 + \boxed{}\, d \leq \boxed{}$$
$$110 - \boxed{} + \boxed{} \leq \boxed{} - \boxed{}$$
$$120d \leq \boxed{}$$
$$\frac{120d}{\boxed{}} \leq \frac{\boxed{}}{\boxed{}}$$
$$d \leq \boxed{}$$

3. How many days can Alice have for her vacation?

On the Back!

4. Staci has $90 to buy clothes. She spends $78 at a department store and wants to buy socks that cost $4 per pair. How many pairs of socks can Staci buy?

Use each term from the list below once to complete each sentence.

variable	equation	constant
inequality	coefficient	two-step

1. In the inequality $5x - 8 > 30$, the integer 5 is the
   _____ of the variable.

2. In any inequality or equation, a number that does not change is a
   _____ .

3. In the inequality $6d + 1 \leq 15$, the letter d is the
   _____ .

4. A mathematical sentence that says that the values of two
   expressions are equal is a(n) _____ .

5. A mathematical sentence that uses $<, \leq, >, \geq,$ or $\neq$ to compare
   two quantities is a(n) _____ .

6. The inequality $4x - 5 \leq -15$ is a(n) _____
   inequality because it requires two different operations to solve.

Write the inequality symbol that best corresponds to each phrase.

7. A minimum of _____

8. At least _____

9. Not more than _____

10. In excess of _____

11. At or below _____

Name ______________________________

Build Mathematical Literacy
6-6

Read the word problem below. Then answer the questions to understand the problem.

On his way to a job site, Spencer stops to buy bags of concrete mix. Each bag weighs 60 pounds. Spencer's truck can carry at most 1,700 pounds, and he already has 320 pounds of tools and other equipment in his truck. What are the possible numbers of bags of concrete mix Spencer can buy?

1. Highlight the question you must answer in order to solve this problem.

2. Underline the information that describes what Spencer puts in his truck.

3. Circle the information that describes the weight Spencer's truck can carry.

4. Which inequality represents the problem? Explain.

   ☐ $320 + 60b \leq 1{,}700$

   ☐ $320 + 60b \geq 1{,}700$

   ☐ $60 + 320b \leq 1{,}700$

   ☐ $60 + 320b \geq 1{,}700$

5. Are negative numbers or fractions reasonable solutions for this problem? Explain.

At a factory, two machines pack bottles into boxes for shipping. Machine A can pack 8 boxes per minute, and Machine B can pack 11 boxes per minute.

1. Before shipment, an inspector found that 7 of the boxes were defective and could not be shipped. At least 200 boxes were approved for shipment. Write and solve an inequality to find the amount of time Machine A spent packing the boxes that were approved for shipment.

2. The factory receives an order for more than 1,100 boxes. Machine B has already packed 55 boxes. Write and solve an inequality to find the amount of time it will take Machine B to pack the additional boxes that are needed for the order, assuming none of the boxes are defective.

3. The manager wants the order described in Exercise 2 packed more quickly, so she decides to use both Machine A and Machine B to prepare the shipment. Write and solve an inequality to find the amount of time it will take both machines to pack the additional boxes. Explain why the answer is reasonable.

4. Both machines have been packing boxes for some time, and the difference between the number of boxes that Machine B has packed and the number of boxes that Machine A has packed is less than 200. Write and solve an inequality to find the possible lengths of time to the nearest second that the machines have been working. Describe the possible solutions.

Name _____

Denny likes to create number puzzles. He says, "I subtracted 4 from my height in inches, multiplied by 3, and then added 33. My answer is greater than the street number of my house." Denny lives at 219 Franklin Street. What are possible values for Denny's height in inches?

Write an inequality to represent Denny's height, h.

Multiply by 3	The difference of Denny's height and 4	Add 33	>	Denny's house number	
3	$\cdot$ $(h-4)$	$+$ 33	$>$	219	

$$3(h-4) + 33 > 219$$
$$3h - 12 + 33 > 219$$
$$3h + 21 > 219$$
$$3h + 21 - 21 > 219 - 21$$
$$3h > 198$$
$$\frac{3h}{3} > \frac{198}{3}$$
$$h > 66$$

Denny is taller than 66 inches.

Denny is 36 years old and his daughter is 7 years old. Denny says, " My age is less than 4 more than twice the sum of my son's age and my daughter's age, in years. What are possible ages in years, a, of Denny's son?

1. Fill in the boxes to write an inequality that represents Denny's son's age, a, in years.

Multiply by 2	The sum of Denny's son's age and his daughter's age	Add 4	<	Denny's age
☐ $\cdot$	$(a +$ ☐ $)$	$+$ ☐	$<$	☐

2. Use the Distributive Property to rewrite the inequality from Exercise 1.

3. Solve the Inequality. What are possible ages of Denny's son?

On the Back!

4. Three times the sum of 2 and the number of points Robbie scored in his last basketball game is at least 36. What are possible numbers of points Robbie scored?

Name _____

Complete the vocabulary chart.

Property	Definition	Example
Addition Property of Inequality	The Addition Property of Inequality states that adding the same number to both sides of an inequality maintains the inequality.	$5(x + 7) - 6.7 \leq 4$ $5(x + 7) - 6.7 + 6.7 \leq 4 + 6.7$
Subtraction Property of Inequality	The Subtraction Property of Inequality states that subtracting the same number from both sides of an inequality maintains the inequality.	
Multiplication Property of Inequality		$\dfrac{6x + 1}{5} \geq 3$ $5\left(\dfrac{6x + 1}{5}\right) \geq 5(3)$
Division Property of Inequality	The Division Property of Inequality states that dividing both sides of an inequality by the same nonzero number maintains the inequality. If dividing both sides by a negative value, reverse the inequality symbol.	

Name _____

**Read the word problem below. Then answer the questions
to understand the problem.**

The soccer team raised $525 to buy a shirt and a pair of
shorts for each of the 20 team members. A pair of shorts
costs $12. If a store offers the team the discount advertised
on the sign, what possible prices can each team member
expect to pay for a shirt?

Team Discount:

Take $35 off the total
cost of your team's order!

1. Describe a complete answer to this problem. Underline the words
   in the problem that support your answer.

2. Circle the information that you can use to write an inequality to
   represent the situation.

3. Let x represent the cost of a shirt. Circle the expression that
   represents the combined cost of a pair of shorts and shirt for
   one team member.

   $12x$

   $12 + x$

   $20x$

   $20(12 + x)$

4. Explain why the inequality $20(12 + x) - 35 \leq 525$ represents the
   situation described in this problem.

Name _____

Diana is training for a marathon. The total miles she runs varies from week to week but follows the pattern described in the table.

Day	Distance (miles)
Monday	x
Tuesday	1 mile less than Monday
Wednesday	2 miles more than Monday
Thursday	Twice Tuesday's distance
Friday	Same as Monday
Saturday	3 miles less than Thursday
Sunday	3 times Monday's distance

1. At the beginning of her training, Diana limited her distance so that she did not run more than 10 miles during the first three days of the week. Write an inequality you can use to find the possible distances Diana may have run on Monday during the first week of training. Solve the inequality. Describe the reasonable solutions.

2. Suppose Diana wants the difference between the distance she runs on Sunday and the distance she runs on Tuesday to be greater than 5 miles. What are possible distances that Diana can run on Monday? Explain how to use your answer to find the possible distances Diana can run on Tuesday and Sunday.

3. Diana wants to run at least 60 miles next week. What are the possible distances she can run on Monday? Describe and graph the reasonable solutions.

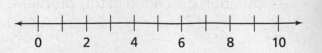